Enrich Workbook with Projects

TEACHER EDITION

Grade 3

SCHOOL PUBLISHERS

Visit *The Learning Site!*
www.harcourtschool.com

CALIFORNIA HSP Math

Printed in the United States of America

ISBN 13: 978-0-15-356935-7
ISBN 10: 0-15-356935-2

1 2 3 4 5 6 7 8 9 10 082 16 15 14 13 12 11 10 09 08 07

Contents

ENRICH PROJECTS

ENRICH WORKSHEETS

UNIT 1: PLACE VALUE, ADDITION AND SUBTRACTION

Chapter 1: Understand Place Value

Chapter 2: Compare, Order, and Round Numbers

Chapter 3: Addition

UNIT 8: CUSTOMARY AND METRIC MEASUREMENT

Chapter 23: Customary Measurement

Chapter 24: Metric Measurement

Enrich Projects

TEACHER NOTES FOR PROJECT

- **Materials:** school calendar, craft sticks, rubber bands, markers for *each group*
- When discussing how to make their place-value displays, students should realize that they can bundle ten sticks together to make ten and that they can bundle ten bundles of ten together to make one hundred.
- Provide at least one copy of the school calendar for each group. Some groups may include copies of the calendar in their displays.
- Provide a generous supply of craft sticks to each group. If craft sticks are not available, or if students run out of craft sticks while making their displays, have them use crayons, straws, or chenille sticks.

Name________________________ Chapter 1

Count with Craft Sticks

Work with your group. Use craft sticks to show the number of days from the first day of school to some important dates during the school year. Make a display for each date.

These craft sticks show 2 tens and 2 ones for the 22nd day of school.

Decide

✓ Choose four important dates from your school calendar.

✓ The value of each craft stick is 1. Discuss with your group's members how to use the sticks to show ten and one hundred. Discuss how you can use rubber bands to bundle the sticks together.

✓ What information does each set of sticks need to display? Make sure that classmates who are not in your group can use your displays to find the number of school days until the dates chosen by your group.

Do

✓ Use a school calendar to count the number of school days from the first day of school to each of your group's four dates.

✓ On a sheet of paper, neatly write the first date and the reason it is important. On the back of the paper, write the number of days from the first day of school to that date. Repeat this step for each date.

✓ Make a display of craft sticks for each date. In each display, use the correct number of sticks to show the number of school days from the first day of school until that date. Be sure to include labels for the ones, tens, and hundreds in your display.

Share

✓ Display each set of craft sticks with the information you wrote about each date. Look at the displays of other groups, and check their work.

EP1 Enrich Project

- Provide paper for students to record the information for their displays.
- Review the *Decide*, *Do*, and *Share* steps for completing the project. Answer questions about the steps before the groups begin their work.

Project Checklist

Evaluate whether each group

_____ cooperatively selects important dates from the school calendar.

_____ accurately displays the correct number of craft sticks for each date selected.

_____ includes written information regarding dates selected and numbers of school days from the first day of school.

_____ neatly arranges information and craft sticks in a meaningful way.

SOLUTIONS FOR EXTENSIONS

1a. 11 times **1b.** 21 times

2. Expanded form and word form are given here. However, students must write each number in two additional ways, for which answers will vary.

a. 20,000 + 9,000 + 300 + 7; twenty-nine thousand, three hundred seven

b. 800,000 + 2,000 + 500 + 20 + 1; eight hundred two thousand, five hundred twenty-one

c. Answers will vary.

3a. 8 **3b.** 110 **3c.** 9 **3d.** 665 **3e.** 37

Name____ **Chapter 1**

Extensions

1. Logical Reasoning

a. If you wrote the numbers from 1 to 100, how many times would you use the digit 0?

b. If you wrote the numbers from 1 to 100, how many times would you use the digit 1?

2. Names for Numbers

You can write numbers in different ways. Here are different ways to write the numbers 32 and 786:

<u>32</u>	<u>785</u>
30 + 2	700 + 80 + 5
thirty-two	seven hundred eighty-five
10 + 10 + 12	1,000 – 215
the next even number greater than 30	one more than 784

Write each number below in four different ways.

a. 29,307 **b.** 802,521 **c.** the last four digits of your phone number

3. Roman Numerals

The ancient Romans used only seven letters to write all numbers. These Roman numerals are still used today. You may see them on clocks and buildings.

I	V	X	L	C	D	M
1	5	10	50	100	500	1,000

Here are some rules for finding the value of Roman numerals.

- When a letter is repeated, add the values.

  III ⟶ $1 + 1 + 1 = 3$

- When a letter with a lesser value follows a letter with a greater value, add the values.

  XVI ⟶ $10 + 5 + 1 = 16$

- When a letter with a greater value follows a letter with a lesser value, subtract the lesser value from the greater value.

  XL ⟶ $50 - 10 = 40$

Write the value of each Roman numeral.

a. VIII b. CX c. IX d. DCLXV e. XXXVII

TEACHER NOTES FOR PROJECT

- **Materials:** 3 number cubes, paper *for each group*
- Tell students that if they cannot form a group with exactly three students, they can adjust the game board accordingly. Groups with only two students can use just the first two columns of the game board. Groups with more than three students can copy the game board onto a separate sheet of paper and add a column for each additional student. Point values for numbers that are made also should be adjusted.
- Review the Decide, Do, and Share steps for completing the project. Answer questions about the steps before the groups begin their work.

Name______________________ Chapter 2

A Number Game

Form a group with two other classmates. Then play the game below by comparing and ordering numbers.

Decide

✓ Decide which group member will go first, second, and third when playing the game.

✓ Discuss the methods you will use to compare and order 3-digit numbers.

Do

✓ Write your names in the boxes at the top of the game board at the right.

✓ Take turns rolling three number cubes. On your turn, use the numbers you rolled and make the greatest possible 3-digit number. Write your number in row A, in the box below your name.

✓ After each player has had a turn, draw a circle around the greatest number in row A. Award 3 points to the player who made that number. Draw a square around the next-greatest number. Award 2 points to the player with that number. Award 1 point to the player who made the least number. Make a score card to keep track of each player's points.

GAME BOARD

	Name	Name	Name
A.			
B.			
C.			
D.			
E.			
F.			
G.			
H.			
I.			
J.			
K.			

✓ Play the game for a total of ten rounds. Add the points for each player. The player with the most points wins.

✓ On a separate sheet of paper, write the numbers in each row in order from least to greatest.

Share

✓ Discuss everyday events in which you have compared or ordered numbers.

EP2 Enrich Project

Project Checklist

Evaluate whether each group

_____ discusses the methods it will use to compare and order 3-digit numbers.

_____ neatly and accurately records the results of each player's turn when playing the game.

_____ plays the game according to the given directions and awards the correct number of points to each player.

_____ orders the resulting numbers from each row of the game board.

_____ discusses everyday events in which each group member has compared or ordered numbers.

SOLUTIONS FOR EXTENSIONS

1. 143; Odd numbers end in 1, 3, 5, 7, or 9. Odd numbers between 140 and 150 = 141, 143, 145, 147, 149. 141 and 143 round to 140, but only 143 does not end in 1.
2. **a.** G **b.** R **c.** A **d.** D **e.** E **f.** R
   g. O **h.** C **i.** K **j.** S **k.** T **l.** H
   m. I **n.** R **o.** D
   The letters spell "THIRD GRADE ROCKS."

Name____________________

Extensions

1. What's the Number?

Max wrote a number on a sheet of paper and then hid the paper behind his back. He gave these clues about the number.

- The number is odd.
- The number does not end in 1.
- The number is greater than 140 and less than 150.
- Rounded to the nearest ten, the number is 140.

What number did Max write? Explain how you know.

2. The Order of Things

Fill in the blank for each question below.

a. What is the first letter of the word GREATER? _____

b. What is the second letter of the word FRACTION? _____

c. What is the third letter of the word GRAPHS? _____

d. What is the fourth letter of the word GRID? _____

e. What is the fifth letter of the word NUMBER? _____

f. What is the sixth letter of the word PROPERTY? _____

g. What is the seventh letter of the word FRACTION? _____

h. What is the eighth letter of the word PERIODIC? _____

i. What is the seventh letter of the word NETWORK? _____

j. What is the sixth letter of the word EXPRESSION? _____

k. What is the fifth letter of the word MINUTE? _____

l. What is the fourth letter of the word MATH? _____

m. What is the third letter of the word HEIGHT? _____

n. What is the second letter of the word PROPERTY? _____

o. What is the first letter of the word DOMAIN? _____

Move your answers for questions *k* through *o* to the beginning of the list. What do the letters spell?

TEACHER NOTES FOR PROJECT

- Make sure that students understand that the tally table shows the total number of each item, such as books, pencils, or erasers. When they answer questions 1–3, they are combining totals of different items (for example, pencils and erasers, or books and pencils).
- If students finish the project early, have them work with their group to find other items in their desks that they have in common. Ask them to repeat the project, using the new items.
- Review the Decide, Do, and Share steps for completing the project. Answer questions about the steps before the groups begin their work.

Name______________________ Chapter 3

Tally Your School Supplies

In the classroom are many items that you can count. In this project, you will count the numbers of books, pencils, and erasers in your desk. You and the other members of your group will record your data in a tally table. Then your group will use addition to find sums of different items.

Decide

✓ Talk about how your group can use a tally table to record its data.

✓ Choose one group member to make a tally table like the one shown below.

Do

✓ Take turns with the members of your group. On your turn, count the numbers of books, pencils, and erasers in your desk. Make tally marks in your group's tally table to show the number of each item in your desk.

Item	Tally Marks	Total
Books	𝍸 𝍸 ||||	
Pencils		
Erasers		

✓ After all the tally marks have been made, find the total number of each item and write it in the table.

✓ As a group, use addition and the tally table to answer questions 1–3 below. Be sure to check your work.

1. What is the total number of pencils and erasers in your group's desks?
2. What is the total number of books and pencils in your group's desks?
3. What is the total number of books, pencils, and erasers in your group's desks?

Share

✓ Exchange tally tables with another group. Answer questions 1–3 above for the other group's table.

EP3 Enrich Project

Project Checklist

Evaluate whether each group

______ counts the numbers of books, pencils, and erasers in its members' desks.

______ makes a tally table with the appropriate column labels and correctly tallies the numbers in its table.

______ finds the sums to answer questions 1–3 of the Do section.

______ exchanges tally tables with another group and uses the new table to answer questions 1–3.

SOLUTIONS FOR EXTENSIONS

1. 28 + 37 = 65; Jeff took bag 2 and bag 3 to obtain a total of 65 beads.

2a. 225, 525; B = 2; A = 5

2b. 770, 707; R = 7; S = 0

3a. 999; 111

3b. 1,110

3c. 987

4. Check students' work.

Extensions

1. **Bead Bags**

   Beads are stored in four bags. Bag 1 contains 20 beads. Bag 2 contains 28 beads. Bag 3 contains 37 beads. Bag 4 contains 24 beads. Jeff takes two bags. There are a total of 65 beads in the two bags altogether. Which bags did Jeff take?

2. **Guess the Digits**

   Each letter below stands for a digit. Find the digits.

   a.
   ```
     BBA
   + ABA
   -----
     750
   ```

   b.
   ```
     RRS
   + RSR
   -----
   1,477
   ```

3. **Logical Reasoning**

   All numbers are made up of the digits 0, 1, 2, 3, 4, 5, 6, 7, 8, and 9.

   a. What is the greatest 3-digit number you can make by repeating the same digit? the least?

   b. What is the sum of the 3-digit numbers you made in part a?

   c. What is the greatest 3-digit number you can make without repeating any digit?

4. **Write Your Own Problems**

   Write three problems that use 3-digit numbers and that require addition to solve. Solve the problems. Then exchange papers with a classmate, and discuss each other's problems and solutions.

TEACHER NOTES FOR PROJECT

- Heart rates and weights shown in the table are averages.
- The animals, arranged in order from fastest heart rate to slowest heart rate, are as follows: chicken, rabbit, monkey, cat, dog (small), dog (large), goat, pig, cow, horse.
- Help students understand that the greater the value of the heart rate, the faster the heart rate.
- Students should discover that small animals have *faster* heart rates than large animals.
- Review the *Decide*, *Do*, and *Share* steps for completing the project. Answer questions before the groups begin their work.

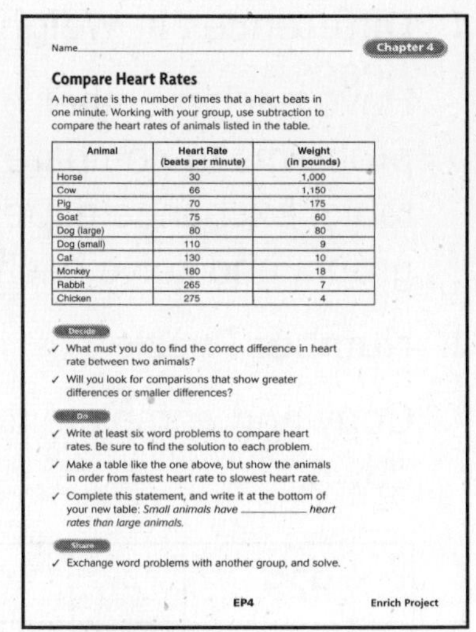

Name____________________ Chapter 4

Compare Heart Rates

A heart rate is the number of times that a heart beats in one minute. Working with your group, use subtraction to compare the heart rates of animals listed in the table.

Animal	Heart Rate (beats per minute)	Weight (in pounds)
Horse	30	1,000
Cow	66	1,150
Pig	70	175
Goat	75	60
Dog (large)	80	80
Dog (small)	110	9
Cat	130	10
Monkey	180	18
Rabbit	265	7
Chicken	275	4

Decide

✓ What must you do to find the correct difference in heart rate between two animals?

✓ Will you look for comparisons that show greater differences or smaller differences?

Do

✓ Write at least six word problems to compare heart rates. Be sure to find the solution to each problem.

✓ Make a table like the one above, but show the animals in order from fastest heart rate to slowest heart rate.

✓ Complete this statement, and write it at the bottom of your new table: *Small animals have ________ heart rates than large animals.*

Share

✓ Exchange word problems with another group, and solve.

EP4 Enrich Project

Project Checklist

Evaluate whether each group

______ accurately uses subtraction to find differences in heart rates

______ writes at least six subtraction problems.

______ analyzes the data its table to find the relationship between heart rate and weight.

______ presents its word problems to another group and solves the other group's problems.

SOLUTIONS FOR EXTENSIONS

1. Check students' word problems and solutions.
2. The missing numbers are 258 in the top row, 462 in the middle row, and 328 in the bottom row.
3. Whenever you subtract a number from another number with the same digits (scrambled), the sum of the digits of the resulting difference should add up to 9 or a multiple of 9. The digits of any multiple of 9 also add up to 9 or a multiple of 9.

Name________________________________

Extensions

1. Differences in Weight

Have each member of your group write three word problems to compare animal weights shown in the table. Exchange papers with the members of your group, and solve each other's problems.

2. Number Puzzle

Copy and complete the puzzle. Subtract across and down.

929	−	☐	=	671
−		−		−
601	−	139	=	☐
=		=		=
☐	−	119	=	209

3. Nine Makes a Difference

Follow these steps:

a. Start with any 3-digit number.

b. Mix up the digits to make a new 3-digit number.

c. Find the difference of the two 3-digit numbers.

d. Add the digits of the difference to form a new number.

e. Add the digits of the new number. Continue until the sum is 9.

Example:

$$\begin{array}{r} 523 \\ -235 \\ \hline 288 \end{array}$$

$2 + 8 + 8 = 18$

$1 + 8 = 9$

No matter what number you start with, you will eventually have a number whose digits have a sum of 9. Choose five other 3-digit numbers, and follow the steps above.

TEACHER NOTES FOR PROJECT

- **Materials:** 2 number cubes labeled 1–6 (see Teacher Resource Book), 1-centimeter grid paper (see Teacher Resource Book), crayons or colored pencils *for each group*
- Students should demonstrate their understanding of arrays before beginning the *Do* step of the project.
- If time allows, have groups repeat the project with a new piece of grid paper. Challenge students to place the arrays so that fewer blank squares are left on the grid paper.
- Review the *Decide*, *Do*, and *Share* steps for completing the project. Answer questions before the groups begin their work.

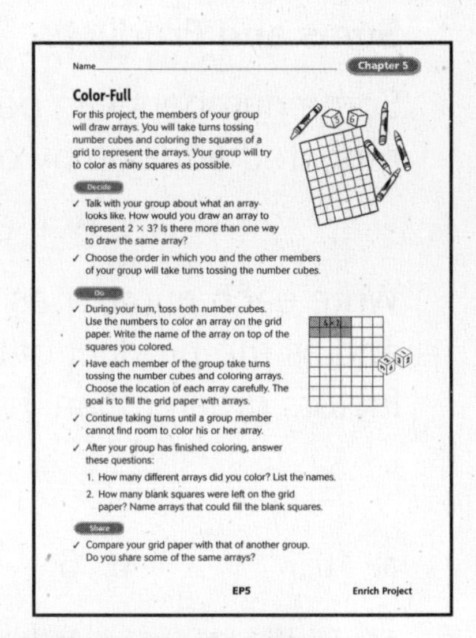
Name________ Chapter 5

Color-Full

For this project, the members of your group will draw arrays. You will take turns tossing number cubes and coloring the squares of a grid to represent the arrays. Your group will try to color as many squares as possible.

Decide

✓ Talk with your group about what an array looks like. How would you draw an array to represent 2 × 3? Is there more than one way to draw the same array?

✓ Choose the order in which you and the other members of your group will take turns tossing the number cubes.

Do

✓ During your turn, toss both number cubes. Use the numbers to color an array on the grid paper. Write the name of the array on top of the squares you colored.

✓ Have each member of the group take turns tossing the number cubes and coloring arrays. Choose the location of each array carefully. The goal is to fill the grid paper with arrays.

✓ Continue taking turns until a group member cannot find room to color his or her array.

✓ After your group has finished coloring, answer these questions:

1. How many different arrays did you color? List the names.
2. How many blank squares were left on the grid paper? Name arrays that could fill the blank squares.

Share

✓ Compare your grid paper with that of another group. Do you share some of the same arrays?

EP5 Enrich Project

Project Checklist

Evaluate whether each group of students:

_____ cooperatively decides the order in which the partners will toss the number cubes.

_____ accurately colors and names each array on the grid paper.

_____ shows evidence of using strategy or logical reasoning to place the arrays on the grid paper in order to achieve the goal of filling the grid paper with arrays.

_____ compares the arrays to those of another group.

SOLUTIONS FOR EXTENSIONS

1a. Possible answers: $10 = 2 + 2 + 2 + 2 + 2$; $10 = 5 + 5$; $10 = 2 \times 5$; $10 = 5 \times 2$

1b. Possible answers: $6 = 2 + 2 + 2$; $6 = 3 + 3$; $6 = 2 \times 3$; $6 = 3 \times 2$

1c. Possible answers: $18 = 6 + 6 + 6$; $18 = 3 + 3 + 3 + 3 + 3 + 3$; $18 = 2 + 2 + 2 + 2 + 2 + 2 + 2 + 2 + 2$; $18 = 9 + 9$; $18 = 6 \times 3$; $18 = 3 \times 6$; $18 = 2 \times 9$; $18 = 9 \times 2$

1d. Possible answers: $12 = 3 + 3 + 3 + 3$; $12 = 4 + 4 + 4$; $12 = 2 + 2 + 2 + 2 + 2 + 2$; $12 = 6 + 6$; $12 = 3 \times 4$; $12 = 4 \times 3$; $12 = 2 \times 6$; $12 = 6 \times 2$

2a.

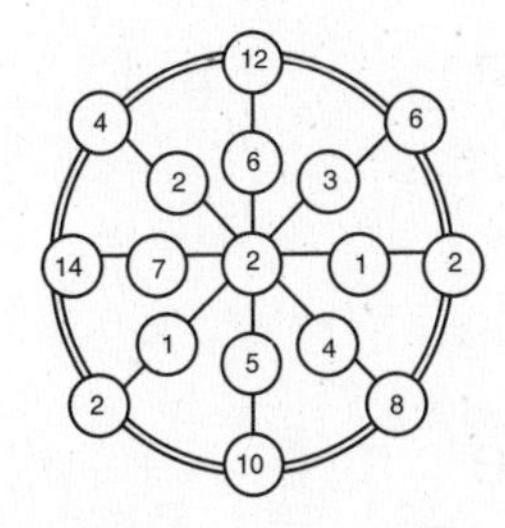

2b.

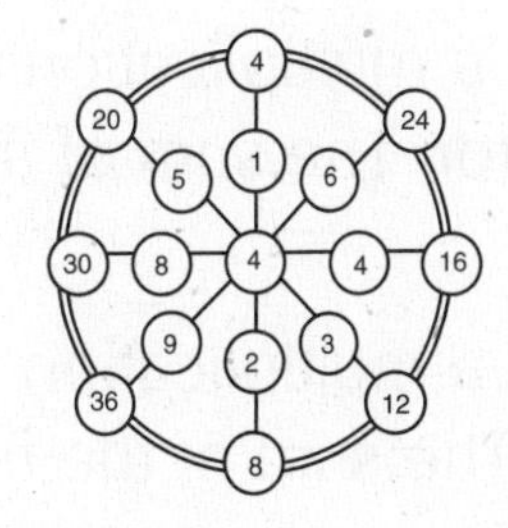

3a. 4 and 7

3b. 2 and 4

Name______________________________ Chapter 5

Extensions

1. Sums and Products

Some numbers can be represented as a sum using repeated addition by or as the product of two factors.

$24 = 6 + 6 + 6 + 6$ $24 = 4 \times 6$

Write each number as a sum using repeated addition and as the product of two factors. Use addends or factors greater than 1.

a. 10 **b.** 6 **c.** 18 **d.** 12

2. Multiplication on Wheels

The number in the center represents one of the factors of a multiplication sentence. The circles on the edge of the wheel represent the products. Write a number in each of the blank circles that will make each multiplication sentence true.

a.

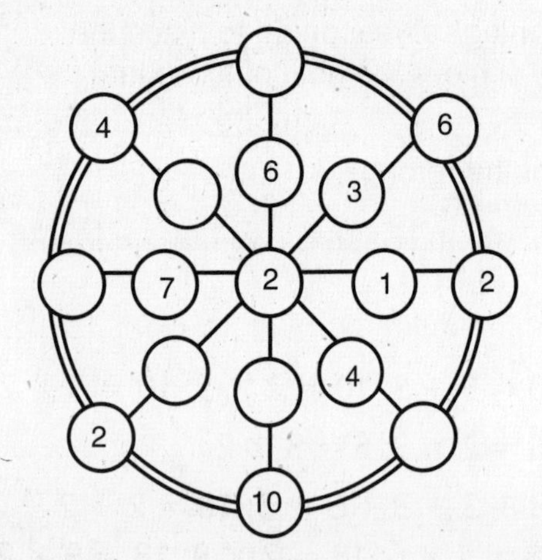

b.

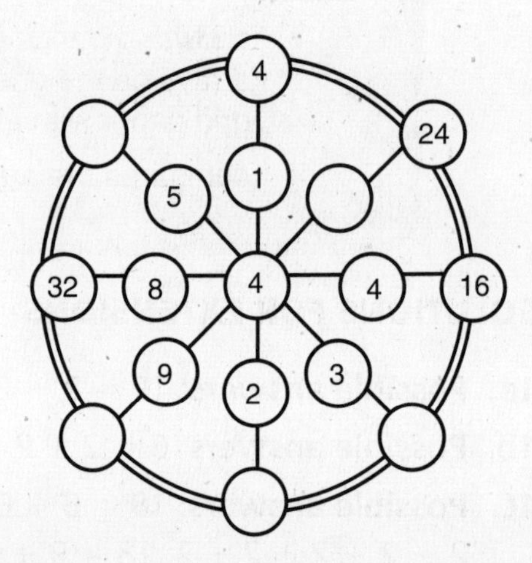

3. Logical Reasoning

a. One factor in a multiplication sentence is 3 more than the other factor. The sum of the factors is 11. What are the factors?

b. One factor in a multiplication sentence is double the other factor. The sum of the factors is 6. What are the factors?

TEACHER NOTES FOR PROJECT

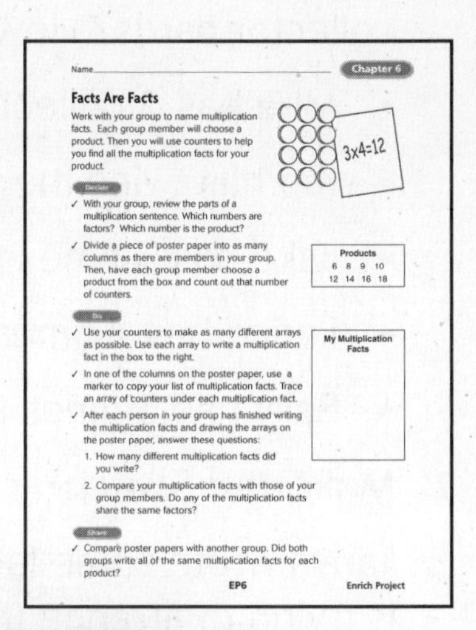
Name____________________ Chapter 6

Facts Are Facts

Work with your group to name multiplication facts. Each group member will choose a product. Then you will use counters to help you find all the multiplication facts for your product.

Decide

✓ With your group, review the parts of a multiplication sentence. Which numbers are factors? Which number is the product?

✓ Divide a piece of poster paper into as many columns as there are members in your group. Then, have each group member choose a product from the box and count out that number of counters.

Products			
6	8	9	10
12	14	16	18

Do

✓ Use your counters to make as many different arrays as possible. Use each array to write a multiplication fact in the box to the right.

✓ In one of the columns on the poster paper, use a marker to copy your list of multiplication facts. Trace an array of counters under each multiplication fact.

✓ After each person in your group has finished writing the multiplication facts and drawing the arrays on the poster paper, answer these questions:

1. How many different multiplication facts did you write?
2. Compare your multiplication facts with those of your group members. Do any of the multiplication facts share the same factors?

My Multiplication Facts

Share

✓ Compare poster papers with another group. Did both groups write all of the same multiplication facts for each product?

EP6 Enrich Project

- **Materials:** adequate supply of counters, poster paper, and markers *for each group of students*
- Students should demonstrate their understanding of the terms factor and product about the steps before beginning the *Do* step of the project.
- Review the *Decide*, *Do*, and *Share* steps for completing the project. Answer questions before the groups begin their work.
- If time allows, have groups repeat the project using different products. Challenge the students to make arrays that form the shape of a square.

Project Checklist

Evaluate whether each group of students:

_____ demonstrates an understanding in discussion of the terms factor and product.

_____ accurately writes and models each array on the poster paper.

_____ answers the discussion questions using the multiplication facts listed on the group's poster paper.

_____ compares the poster paper to that of another group and identifies similarities between them.

SOLUTIONS FOR EXTENSIONS

1. Jake has the most cards; Mira, 2; Kip, 4; Lance, 8; Sally, 20; Jake, 24

2.

4	×	6	=	4		6	×	5	=	18
3	×	3	=	15		5	×	24	=	20

3a. 15 bouncy balls, 10 kazoos

3b. 4 packages of bouncy balls, 5 packages of party hats, 2 packages of bubbles

3c. more; 4

Extensions

1. Logical Reasoning

Use the clues below. Who has the greatest number of collector cards? How many cards does each person have?

- Mira has 2 collector cards.
- Kip has twice the number of cards that Mira has.
- Jake has 3 times the number of cards Lance has.
- Lance has 4 times the number of cards that Mira has.
- Sally has 5 times the number of cards Kip has.

2. Make the Switch

Tanya wrote some factors and products on index cards. She is trying to arrange them to make multiplication sentences.

4	×	6	=	4
3	×	3	=	15

6	×	5	=	18
5	×	24	=	20

What two pairs of cards should Tanya switch so that her multiplication sentences are correct? Draw a line between the cards that should be switched.

3. Shane Goes Shopping

Shane is buying party favors at Joe's Party Warehouse. The table shows how many party favors are in each package.

a. Shane decides to buy 3 packages of bouncy balls and 5 packages of kazoos. How many of each item will he have?

b. Suppose Shane will have 20 guests at his party. How many packages of bouncy balls, party hats, and bubbles will he need to buy?

c. If Shane buys 4 packages of silly straws, will he have more or less than 20 straws? How many more or less?

Joe's Party Warehouse	
Item	**Number per Package**
Bouncy balls	5
Party hats	4
Bubbles	10
Silly straws	6
Kazoos	2

TEACHER NOTES FOR PROJECT

- **Materials:** 5 pieces of poster board, glue, and an adequate supply of index cards *for each group of students*
- Discuss with students how strategies can be useful when solving a problem. You may choose to have a class discussion to review some of the multiplication strategies that students already have learned.
- Review the *Decide, Do*, and *Share* steps for completing the project. Answer questions about the stepsbefore the groups begin their work.
- Provide space for groups to display their projects.

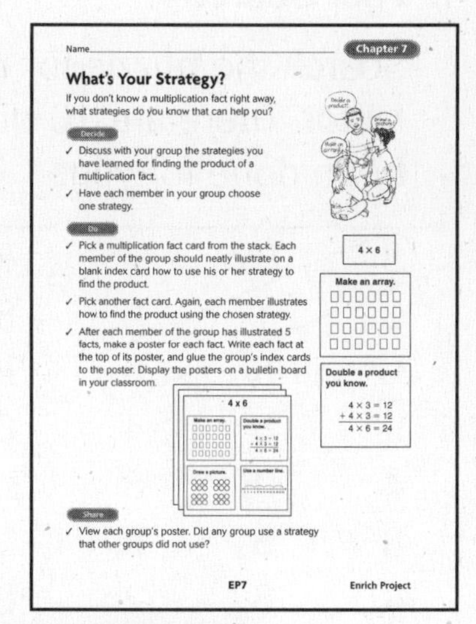

Name

Chapter 7

What's Your Strategy?

If you don't know a multiplication fact right away, what strategies do you know that can help you?

Decide

✓ Discuss with your group the strategies you have learned for finding the product of a multiplication fact.

✓ Have each member in your group choose one strategy.

Do

✓ Pick a multiplication fact card from the stack. Each member of the group should neatly illustrate on a blank index card how to use his or her strategy to find the product.

✓ Pick another fact card. Again, each member illustrates how to find the product using the chosen strategy.

✓ After each member of the group has illustrated 5 facts, make a poster for each fact. Write each fact at the top of its poster, and glue the group's index cards to the poster. Display the posters on a bulletin board in your classroom.

Share

✓ View each group's poster. Did any group use a strategy that other groups did not use?

EP7 Enrich Project

Project Checklist

Evaluate whether each group of students:

______ uses discussion to review the multiplication strategies they have learned.

______ cooperatively decides which student will illustrate which strategy.

______ accurately models each multiplication fact on an index card using the strategies learned.

______ neatly arranges each set of index cards on each piece of poster board.

______ compares poster boards with other groups of students.

SOLUTIONS FOR EXTENSIONS

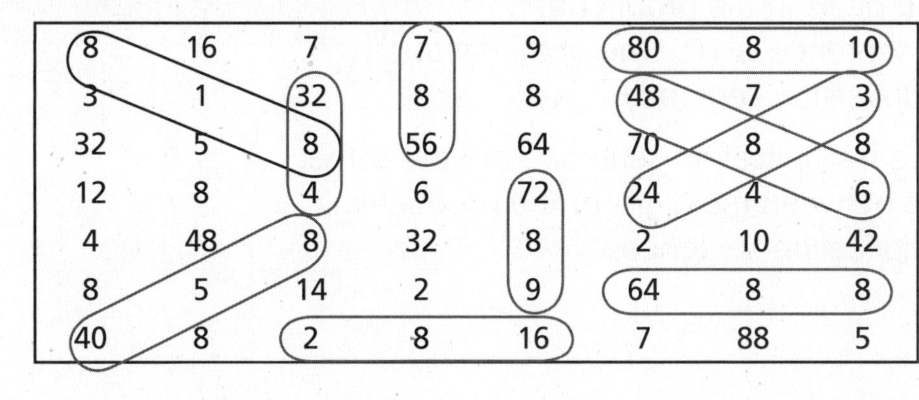

8	16	7	7	9	80	8	10
3	1	32	8	8	48	7	3
32	5	8	56	64	70	8	8
12	8	4	6	72	24	4	6
4	48	8	32	8	2	10	42
8	5	14	2	9	64	8	8
40	8	2	8	16	7	88	5

2a. 36
2b. greater than
2c. 8×9
2d. 126
3a. $7 \times 4 = 28$
3b. $8 \times 8 = 64$

Name______________________________

Extensions

1. Fact Search

Search the puzzle for multiplication facts that have 8 as a factor. There are 10 different facts in all. The first one has been done for you.

8	16	7	7	9	80	8	10
3	1	32	8	8	48	7	3
32	5	8	56	64	70	8	8
12	8	4	6	72	24	4	6
4	48	8	32	8	2	10	42
8	5	14	2	9	64	8	8
40	8	2	8	16	7	88	5

2. Spin a Product

Camila has an 8-section spinner labeled 1–8. She will multiply the number she spins by 9.

a. What will be the product if Camila spins a 4?

b. If Camila spins a 6, will the product be less than or greater than 50?

c. Suppose Camila first spins a 3 and then spins an 8. Which product will have an even number?

d. Camila spins a 2, 5, and 7. If Camila finds the sum of all 3 products, what will be her total?

3. Logical Reasoning

a. The sum of the digits in the product of a multiplication sentence is 10. One of the factors is 7. Write the multiplication sentence.

b. The factors in a multiplication sentence are the same. The difference between the digits of the product is 2. Write the multiplication sentence.

TEACHER NOTES FOR PROJECT

- **Materials:** adequate supply of counters *for each group of students*
- Students should have an understanding of how to make an array before beginning the *Do* step of the project.
- You may choose to demonstrate making one combination for students to ensure understanding.
- Review the *Decide, Do*, and *Share* steps for completing the project. Answer questions before the groups begin their work.
- If time allows, challenge groups to repeat the project using larger groups such as 4 and 5.

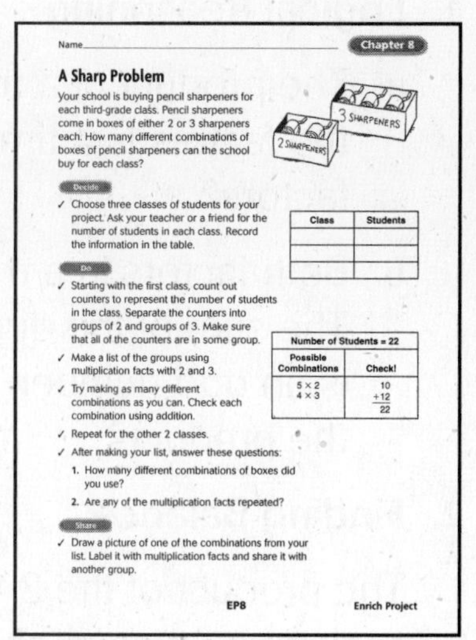

Name____________________ Chapter 8

A Sharp Problem

Your school is buying pencil sharpeners for each third-grade class. Pencil sharpeners come in boxes of either 2 or 3 sharpeners each. How many different combinations of boxes of pencil sharpeners can the school buy for each class?

Decide

✓ Choose three classes of students for your project. Ask your teacher or a friend for the number of students in each class. Record the information in the table.

Class	Students

Do

✓ Starting with the first class, count out counters to represent the number of students in the class. Separate the counters into groups of 2 and groups of 3. Make sure that all of the counters are in some group.

✓ Make a list of the groups using multiplication facts with 2 and 3.

✓ Try making as many different combinations as you can. Check each combination using addition.

Number of Students = 22	
Possible Combinations	Check!
5×2 4×3	10 +12 22

✓ Repeat for the other 2 classes.

✓ After making your list, answer these questions:

1. How many different combinations of boxes did you use?
2. Are any of the multiplication facts repeated?

Share

✓ Draw a picture of one of the combinations from your list. Label it with multiplication facts and share it with another group.

EP8 Enrich Project

Project Checklist

Evaluate whether each group of students:

_____ cooperatively assigns each group member a job, or task, for the project.

_____ accurately models each combination with counters and records the combination as multiplication sentences.

_____ checks the accuracy of each combination by multiplying then finding the sum of the products.

_____ answers the discussion questions using the combinations on the group's lists.

_____ draws a combination from the list and shares it with another group.

SOLUTIONS FOR EXTENSIONS

1a. 8 and 2

1b. 7 and 7; 49

2a. 6

2b. 1

2c. 2

2d. 3

3a. 5

3b. 33

Name________________________________

Extensions

1. Logical Reasoning

a. The product of a multiplication sentence is 16. One of the factors is 4 times the other. What are the two factors?

b. Both factors in a multiplication sentence are the same. The sum of the digits in the product is 13. The product is an odd number. What are the two factors? What is the product?

2. Finding Balance

The product of the 3 factors on the left side of each scale should equal the product of the 3 factors on the right side of each scale. There is one missing factor on each scale.

Choose a factor from the box that will make both sides of the scale have the same product.

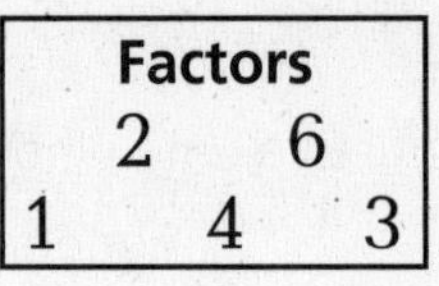

a. 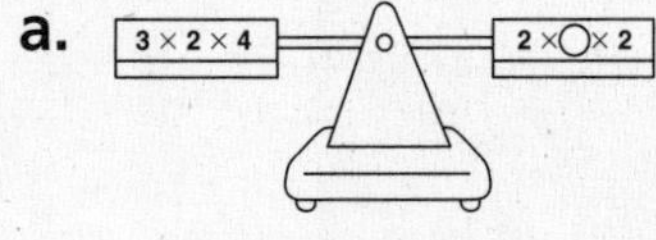

b. 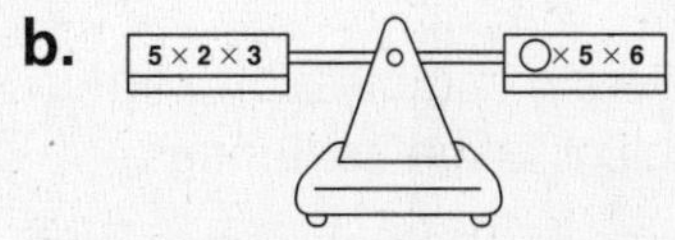

c. 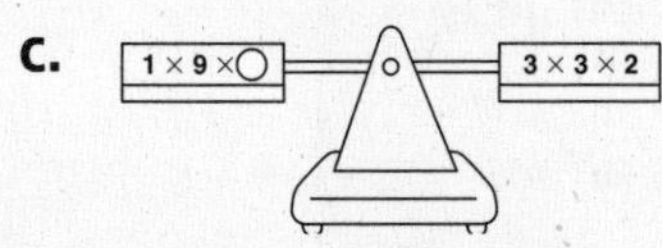

d. 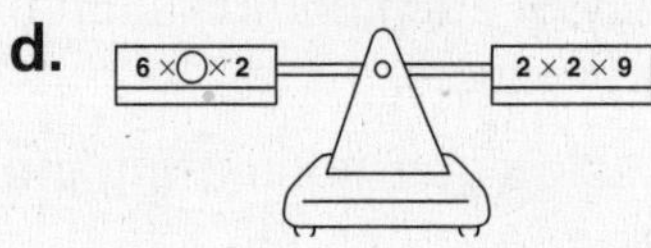

3. Problem Solving

a. Jess came to school with a box of 24 pencils to share. He gave Sandy 4 pencils. Mark got twice as many pencils as Sandy. Jess gave Tara one fewer pencil than Mark. How many pencils does Jess have left?

b. Mr. Keller is shopping for plants to put in his garden. First, he picked up 8 petunias and 6 daisies and placed them in his shopping cart. He then picked up 3 times as many marigolds as daisies. He chose 3 rose bushes, but decided to put 2 of the marigolds back. How many plants are in Mr. Keller's shopping cart?

TEACHER NOTES FOR PROJECT

- **Materials:** adequate supply of counters, 1–15 numeral cards (see Teacher Resource Book), and 1–4 spinner *for each group of students*
- Students should have a basic understanding of the meaning of division before beginning the *Do* step of the project.
- Remind students that after the counters are separated to represent the number on the card, all of the separated counters must be used to have equal groups.
- Review the *Decide, Do,* and *Share* steps for completing the project. Answer questions add the steps before the groups begin their work.

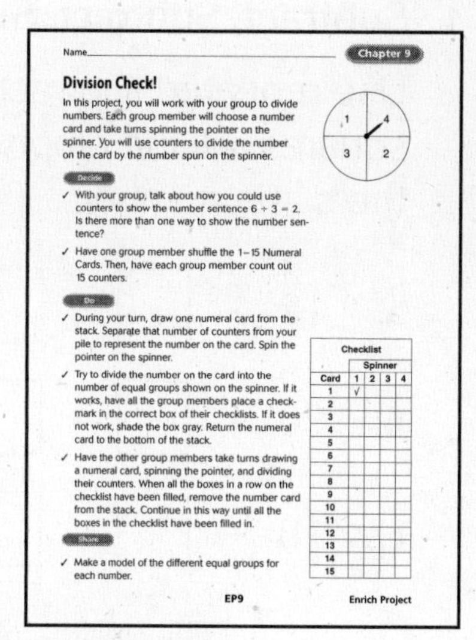

Name__________ Chapter 9

Division Check!

In this project, you will work with your group to divide numbers. Each group member will choose a number card and take turns spinning the pointer on the spinner. You will use counters to divide the number on the card by the number spun on the spinner.

Decide

✓ With your group, talk about how you could use counters to show the number sentence $6 \div 3 = 2$. Is there more than one way to show the number sentence?

✓ Have one group member shuffle the 1–15 Numeral Cards. Then, have each group member count out 15 counters.

Do

✓ During your turn, draw one numeral card from the stack. Separate that number of counters from your pile to represent the number on the card. Spin the pointer on the spinner.

✓ Try to divide the number on the card into the number of equal groups shown on the spinner. If it works, have all the group members place a checkmark in the correct box of their checklists. If it does not work, shade the box gray. Return the numeral card to the bottom of the stack.

✓ Have the other group members take turns drawing a numeral card, spinning the pointer, and dividing their counters. When all the boxes in a row on the checklist have been filled, remove the number card from the stack. Continue in this way until all the boxes in the checklist have been filled in.

Share

✓ Make a model of the different equal groups for each number.

Checklist

Card	Spinner 1	2	3	4
1	√			
2				
3				
4				
5				
6				
7				
8				
9				
10				
11				
12				
13				
14				
15				

EP9 Enrich Project

Project Checklist

Evaluate whether each group of students:

_____ cooperatively decides the order in which group members will take turns.

_____ accurately models each dividend with counters.

_____ demonstrates an understanding of dividing a number of counters into equal groups.

_____ answers the discussion questions using the checklist.

_____ makes a model of the different equal groups to share.

SOLUTIONS FOR EXTENSIONS

1a. 4, 4, 4

1b. 5, 5, 5, 5

1c. 3, 3, 3, 3, 3, 3

2a.

		4	×	6	=	24		
				÷				
8	÷	4	=	2				
				=				
				3	×	9	=	27

2b.

	21				
36	÷	9	=	4	
÷	7			×	
6	=			7	
=	3	×	8	=	24
6				28	

3a. 4 squeaky toys and 2 balls

3b. 6 packs; 36 chewy toys

Name____ **Chapter 9**

Extensions

1. Subtract, Subtract, Subtract

Use repeated subtraction to complete the empty squares. All the empty squares in each row must have the same number.

a. 12 − ☐ − ☐ − ☐ = 0

b. 20 − ☐ − ☐ − ☐ − ☐ = 0

c. 18 − ☐ − ☐ − ☐ − ☐ − ☐ − ☐ = 0

2. Missing Number Puzzles

Complete each puzzle to make the multiplication and division sentences true.

a.

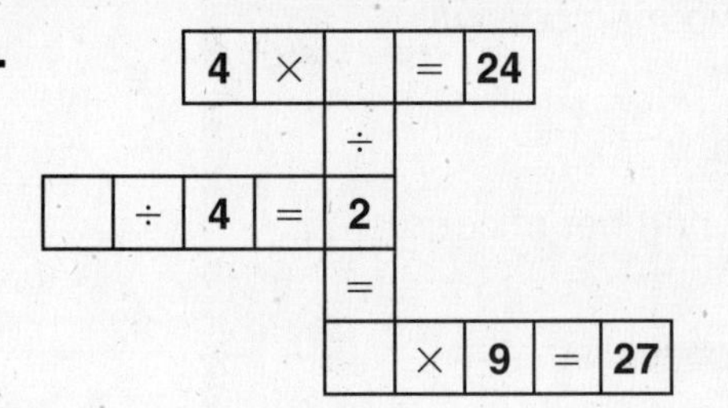

b.

36 ÷ 9 = ☐
÷ 7 ×
☐ = 7
= 3 × ☐ = 24
6 28

3. Patty's Pet Store

Nick took a trip to Patty's Pet Store to buy some new toys and supplies for his 3 dogs. He has $24 to spend in the store.

PATTY'S PET STORE	
Item	**Cost**
Chewy toys – pack of 6	$4
Squeaky toys – bag of 12	$6
Grooming brush	$7
Balls – bag of 6	$3
Collar	$8

a. Nick is thinking of buying a bag of squeaky toys and a bag of balls. If he divides the toys equally among his dogs, how many would each dog receive?

b. Suppose Nick wants to spend all of his money on chewy toys. How many packs of chewy toys could Nick buy? How many chewy toys would he have in all?

TEACHER NOTES FOR PROJECT

- **Materials:** adequate supply of index cards *for each group of students*
- Students should have a basic understanding of fact families before beginning the *Do* step of the project.
- Review the *Decide*, *Do*, and Share steps for completing the project. Answer questions before the groups begin their work.
- If time permits, have students draw a model of the desk arrangement they like best. Have them label the model using division and multiplication sentences then display it for the class.

Name__________ Chapter 10

Desk Division

Work with a partner to divide the desks in a classroom into equal groups. Use index cards to model the possible arrangements of desks. Record your models as division and multiplication sentences.

Decide

✓ Discuss fact families with your partner. How would you write a fact family for the numbers 3, 6, and 18?

✓ With your partner, count out index cards into stacks of 20, 24, and 30. Make three charts like the ones shown below.

Do

✓ Start with the stack of 20 cards. With your partner, model one way to divide the cards into equal groups.

✓ After you make the model, write your model as a division sentence. Then write your model as a multiplication sentence.

Total Number of Desks	Desks in Each Group	Number of Groups
20	÷ 5	= 4

Number of Groups	Desks in Each Group	Total Number of Desks
4	× 5	= 20

✓ Make as many different models as possible for the stack of 20 cards. Record them as division and multiplication sentences.

✓ Repeat the process for the stacks of 24 cards and 30 cards. Record the models in the chart.

Share

✓ Can you make a model of the number of desks in your classroom using equal groups? Share with the class how you could do it, or why you could not.

EP10 Enrich Project

Project Checklist

Evaluate whether each pair of students:

_____ engages in a discussion about fact families and cooperatively writes an example.

_____ accurately models equal groups of index cards.

_____ demonstrates an understanding of fact families by recording each model as division and multiplication sentences.

_____ answers the discussion questions.

_____ decides through discussion whether a model of equal groups using the number of desks in their own classroom can be made.

SOLUTIONS FOR EXTENSIONS

1. Numbers that can be divided by 2 | Numbers that can be divided by 5

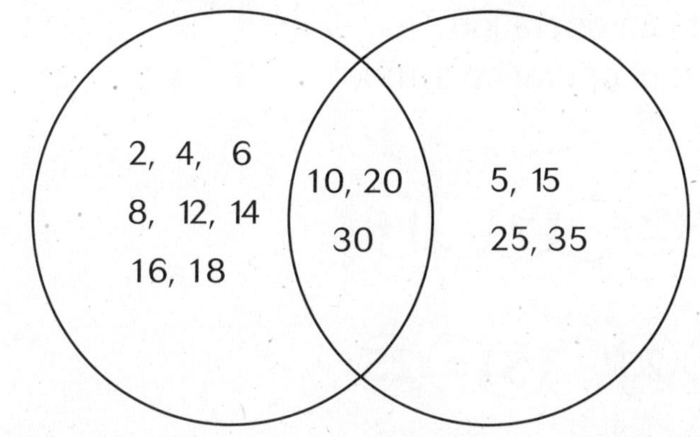

2a. $27 \div 3 = 9$

2b. $16 \div 4 = 4$

3a. $12 - 4 = 8 \div 4 = 2 \times 7 = 14$

3b. $28 \div 7 = 4 \times 5 = 20 + 5 = 25$

Name______________________________

Extensions

1. Sorting Stars

Use the Venn diagram to sort the numbers on each of the stars. Use counters to help you.

Write the numbers that can be divided by 2 in the circle on the left. Write the numbers that can be divided by 5 in the circle on the right. Write the numbers that can be divided by both 2 and 5 in the space where the circles overlap.

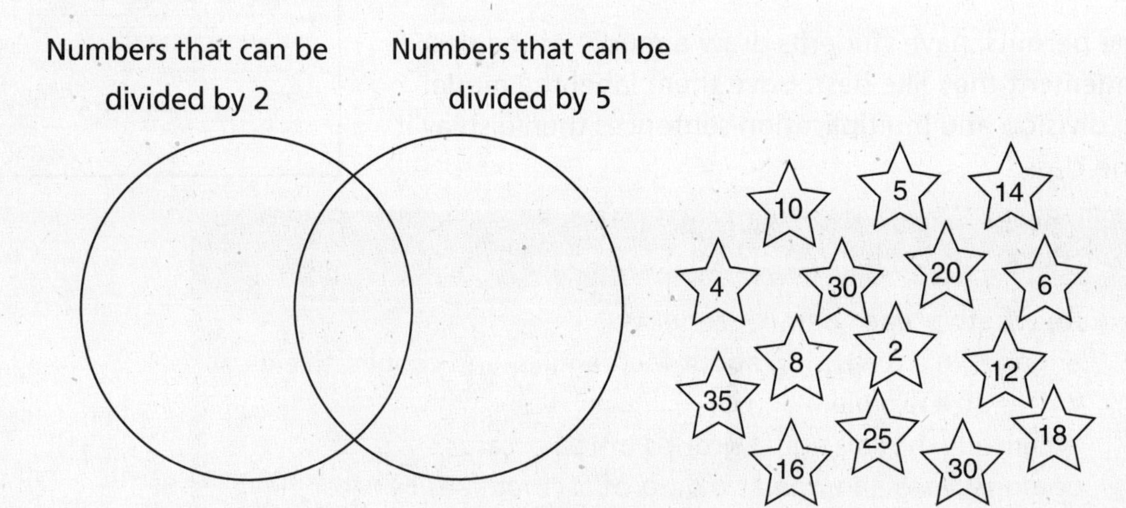

2. Logical Reasoning

a. The quotient in a division fact is 9. The divisor is 6 less than the quotient. What is the division fact?

b. The divisor and the quotient in a division fact are the same. The sum of the digits in the dividend is 7. What is the division fact?

3. Stepping Stones

Each blank stepping stone is missing an operation symbol: +, −, ×, or ÷. Write the correct operation symbol on each blank stepping stone.

a. 

b. 

TEACHER NOTES FOR PROJECT

- **Materials:** connecting cubes, paper *for each group*
- Provide students with a sufficient number of connecting cubes to model the given situations.
- Emphasize the idea of equal groups with students. Students should understand that when items are placed in equal groups, there are no items left over.
- Review the *Decide, Do,* and *Share* steps for completing the project. Answer questions about the steps before the groups begin their work.

Name________________ Chapter 11

Doggie Day Spa

Work with your group to divide the dogs at Daria's Doggie Day Spa into equal groups for walks. Use connecting cubes to model equal groups and solve the problem.

Decide

✓ With your group, talk about equal groups. Name some situations where you might use equal groups.

✓ Read the problem:

Daria takes groups of dogs at her Doggie Day Spa for a walk each day. Daria can take the dogs for a walk in equal groups of 3, 4, or 5. Which size groups can Daria use for each day of the week?

✓ Decide how your group members will take turns modeling equal groups using connecting cubes.

DARIA'S DOGGIE DAY SPA	
Day	Number of Dogs
Monday	18
Tuesday	10
Wednesday	8
Thursday	12
Friday	15

Do

✓ Have one group member use the counting cubes to model the number of dogs on Monday. Then try to divide the stack into 3 equal groups. Does it work? If it does, circle the number 3 in the chart. If it does not, place an X over the number 3. Now try to make models of 4 and 5 equal groups.

✓ Take turns with your group members to find which size groups will work for the other days of the week.

Monday 3 4 5
Tuesday 3 4 5
Wednesday 3 4 5
Thursday 3 4 5
Friday 3 4 5

Share

✓ Have each member of your group choose one day of the week. Draw a picture of the equal groups that Daria could use for that day. Share the pictures with your classmates.

EP11 Enrich Project

Project Checklist

Evaluate whether each group of students:

_____ cooperatively decides the order in which the partners will take turns modeling equal groups.

_____ discusses the idea of equal groups and situations where equal groups might be required.

_____ accurately models equal groups by using connecting cubes and correctly records their findings in the chart.

_____ draws a picture to depict equal groups accurately and shares it with other student groups.

SOLUTIONS FOR EXTENSIONS

1. groups of 4; 6 equal groups of watermelon; 5 equal groups of cantaloupe

2a. stack 1: add 1, stack 2: add 3, stack 3: take away 1; stack 1: add 2, stack 2: add 4, stack 3: neither

2b. 6 blocks in each stack

3a. $14 + 6 = 20 \div 5 = 4 \times 7 = 28$

3b. $35 - 8 = 27 \div 3 = 9 + 8 = 17$

3c. $8 \times 3 = 24 - 6 = 18 \div 6 = 3$

Name______________________________________

Extensions

1. Fruit on Display

Every Monday, a shipment of fruit arrives at a grocery store. The store clerk puts the fruit on display in equal groups of 3, 4, 5, or 6.

Suppose a shipment of 24 watermelons and 20 cantaloupes arrives at the store. The clerk wants to display both fruits by using same-size equal groups. What size equal groups should the clerk use? How many equal groups will there be of watermelons? How many equal groups will there be of cantaloupes?

2. Block Problem

Alicia is making stacks of blocks. She wants each stack to have the same number of blocks.

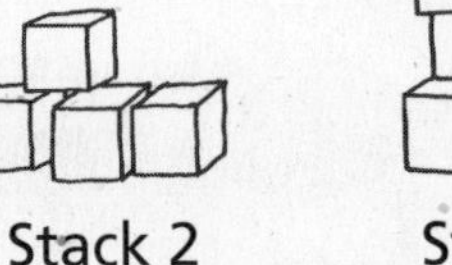

Stack 1 Stack 2 Stack 3

a. How many blocks will Alicia need to add or take away from each stack so that her stacks of blocks are in equal groups of 7? In equal groups of 8?

b. Suppose Alicia doesn't have more blocks to add. If she only can rearrange the blocks to make equal groups, what is the greatest number of blocks that can be in each stack?

3. Equation Chains

Look at each chain of equations. Which operations will make all the equations true for each chain?

Write +, −, ×, or ÷ in each empty link of the chain.

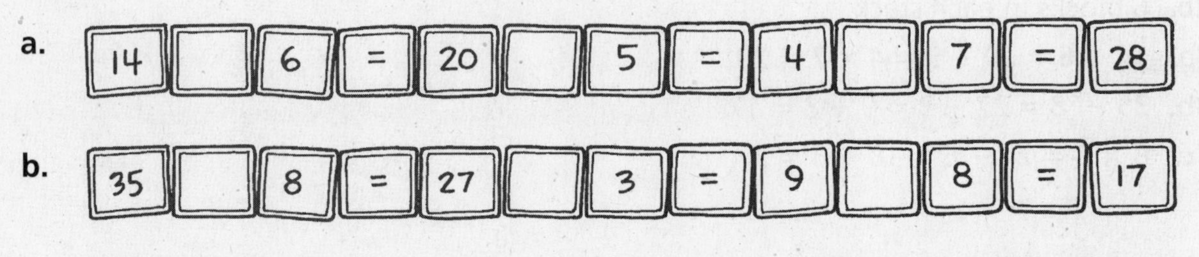

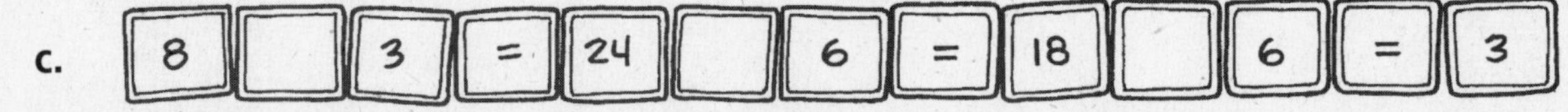

TEACHER NOTES FOR PROJECT

- **Materials:** plane-figure patterns, tagboard, paper, scissors, hole punch, yarn, tape, glue
- Make sure students understand the differences among triangles, squares, circles, and rectangles.
- Students should recognize that plane figures can be grouped by type, including rectangles, triangles, squares, and circles.
- Review the *Decide*, *Do*, and *Share* steps for completing the project. Answer questions about the steps before the groups begin their work.
- If groups finish the project early, have group members trace and cut out more plane figures create a collage by taping or gluing the figures onto paper.

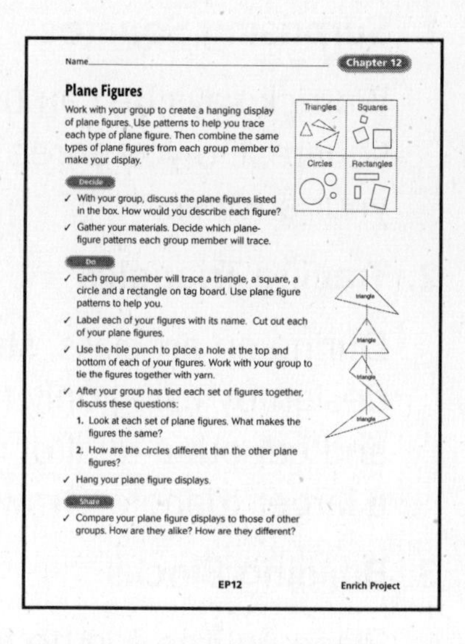
Name________________ Chapter 12

Plane Figures

Work with your group to create a hanging display of plane figures. Use patterns to help you trace each type of plane figure. Then combine the same types of plane figures from each group member to make your display.

Decide

✓ With your group, discuss the plane figures listed in the box. How would you describe each figure?

✓ Gather your materials. Decide which plane-figure patterns each group member will trace.

Do

✓ Each group member will trace a triangle, a square, a circle and a rectangle on tag board. Use plane figure patterns to help you.

✓ Label each of your figures with its name. Cut out each of your plane figures.

✓ Use the hole punch to place a hole at the top and bottom of each of your figures. Work with your group to tie the figures together with yarn.

✓ After your group has tied each set of figures together, discuss these questions:

1. Look at each set of plane figures. What makes the figures the same?
2. How are the circles different than the other plane figures?

✓ Hang your plane figure displays.

Share

✓ Compare your plane figure displays to those of other groups. How are they alike? How are they different?

EP12 Enrich Project

Project Checklist

Evaluate whether each group

_____ accurately describes each plane figure shown in the box.

_____ works collaboratively to trace, cut out, and build their display.

_____ correctly responds to questions 1–3 of the Do section.

_____ compares their plane figure hanging display with other groups.

SOLUTIONS FOR EXTENSIONS

1. no; possible answer: there is no way to arrange five squares so they form a new square. Warrick could use four squares.

2. Check students' drawings.

3a–3c. Answers will vary. Check students' work.

4a–4c. Check students' drawings.

Name____________________

Extensions

1. Surprising Squares

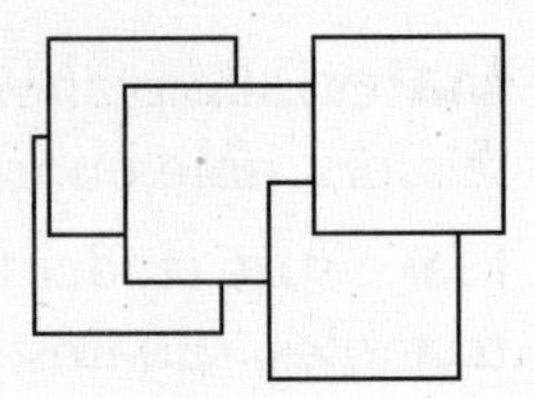

Warrick says he can use five squares to make a larger square. Do you agree? Write *yes* or *no*. If no, explain your answer.

2. Tracing Triangles

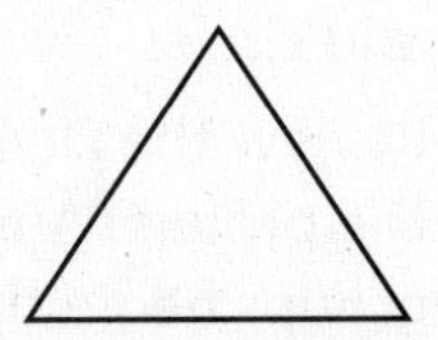

During an art class, students were asked to create a design by using only triangles. Paula decided to trace and cut out a total of nine equilateral triangles to make a larger triangle. Draw a picture to show Paula's design.

3. Building Blocks

Plane figures can be found all around us. Examples of plane figures can be found even in your classroom. Select any two walls from your classroom. For each wall,

a. tell all the different plane figures you see.

b. record the total number of each type of plane figure you found.

c. make a table to display your findings.

4. Create Your Own Art

Art is a fun way to explore mathematics and plane figures. Draw and color your own design of plane figures. Include at least one of each of these figures in your design:

a. a figure with three acute angles

b. a figure with two sets of parallel sides

c. a figure with four sides all the same length

TEACHER NOTES FOR PROJECT

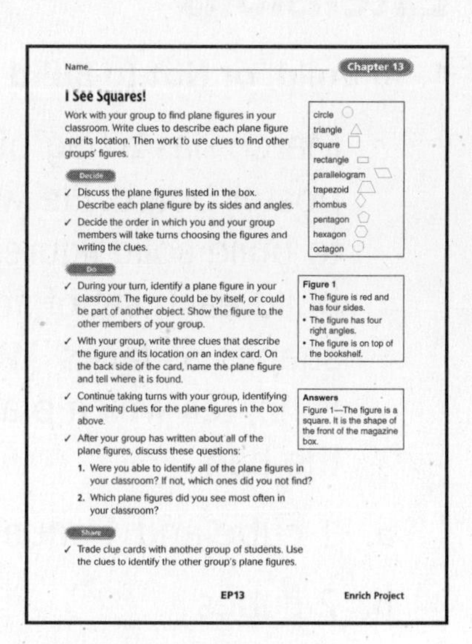

Name______________________ Chapter 13

I See Squares!

Work with your group to find plane figures in your classroom. Write clues to describe each plane figure and its location. Then work to use clues to find other groups' figures.

circle
triangle
square
rectangle
parallelogram
trapezoid
rhombus
pentagon
hexagon
octagon

Decide

✓ Discuss the plane figures listed in the box. Describe each plane figure by its sides and angles.

✓ Decide the order in which you and your group members will take turns choosing the figures and writing the clues.

Do

✓ During your turn, identify a plane figure in your classroom. The figure could be by itself, or could be part of another object. Show the figure to the other members of your group.

✓ With your group, write three clues that describe the figure and its location on an index card. On the back side of the card, name the plane figure and tell where it is found.

✓ Continue taking turns with your group, identifying and writing clues for the plane figures in the box above.

✓ After your group has written about all of the plane figures, discuss these questions:

1. Were you able to identify all of the plane figures in your classroom? If not, which ones did you not find?
2. Which plane figures did you see most often in your classroom?

Figure 1
- The figure is red and has four sides.
- The figure has four right angles.
- The figure is on top of the bookshelf.

Answers
Figure 1—The figure is a square. It is the shape of the front of the magazine box.

Share

✓ Trade clue cards with another group of students. Use the clues to identify the other group's plane figures.

EP13 Enrich Project

- **Materials:** index cards
- Students should be able to identify and describe each plane figure by its sides and angles for students to write clues accurately.
- Review the *Decide, Do,* and *Share* steps for completing the project. Answer questions about the steps before the groups begin their work.
- If groups finish early, have them combine all clue cards into one pile. Students can then be led in a game of Around-the-World by using the clue cards to check students' knowledge of plane figures.

Project Checklist

Evaluate whether each group of students:

_____ discusses each plane figure in the box.

_____ writes clues that accurately describe each plane figure and its location.

_____ collaboratively answers questions 1–2 of the *Do* section.

_____ exchanges clue cards with another group and uses the clues to identify that group's plane figures.

SOLUTIONS FOR EXTENSIONS

1a. yes **1b.** no; 4 squares **1c.** yes **1d.** no; 1 triangle

2a. square pyramid, cube, cone, rectangular prism **2b.** rectangular prism, cube, square pyramid, cylinder

3a. square, square, square **3b.** circle rectangle **3c.** square, rectangle, **3d.** triangle, triangle, triangle

Extensions

1. To Build, or Not to Build

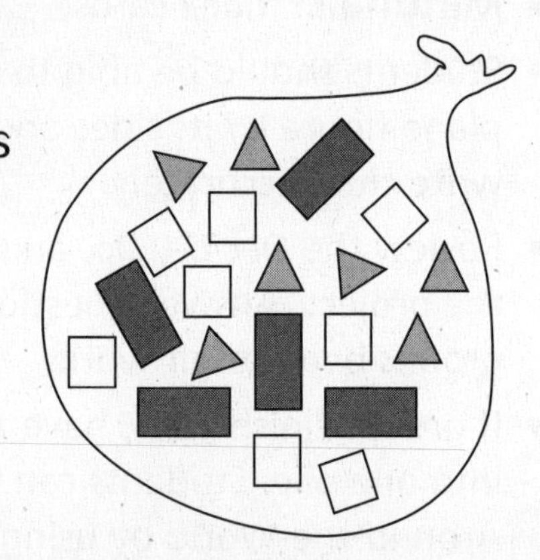

Marco has a bag of plane figures cut from poster board. He wants to use the plane figures to build solid figures. Tell whether Marco can build each set of solid figures by using the shapes as faces. Write *yes* or *no*. If the answer is no, tell which plane figures are missing from the bag.

a. 1 cube and 1 square pyramid

b. 2 cubes

c. 1 rectangular prism and 1 square pyramid

d. 2 square pyramids

2. Logical Reasoning

a. Jenna used a cube, a square pyramid, a rectangular prism, and a cone to make a row of solid figures. The first solid figure in the row has 5 faces. The cube is not the last figure. The third figure has the fewest faces. What is the order of the four solid figures?

b. Larry made his row of solid figures by using a cylinder, a rectangular prism, a cube and a square pyramid. The first solid figure in his row has 8 vertices. The last figure has faces that are the shape of circles. The rectangular prism comes before the cube. What is the order of the four solid figures?

3. Paint Problem

Celia painted the faces of some solid figures blue. She painted all the faces she could see from the view shown without moving the figures. Name the faces on each figure that Celia did not paint.

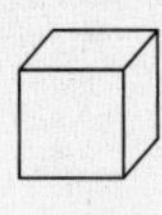

a.

b.

c.

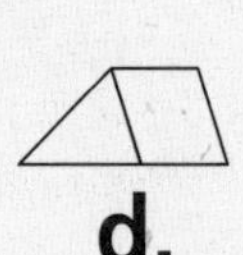

d.

TEACHER NOTES FOR PROJECT

- **Materials:** measuring tape, cotton balls, masking tape, chart paper *for each group of students*
- Students should have an understanding of the relationship between inches, feet and yards before beginning the *Do* step of the project.
- You may wish to demonstrate how to use a measuring tool to measure lengths that are greater than the tool itself (i.e., measuring 14 inches with a 12-inch ruler).
- Review the *Decide*, *Do*, and *Share* steps for completing the project. Answer questions about the steps before the groups begin their work.

Name____________________ Chapter 14

Cotton-Ball Toss

The world record for throwing a 16-pound metal shot put ball is almost 76 feet! Your group will have a cotton-ball-tossing competition, and will measure the lengths of tosses in yards, feet, and inches. The person who can most closely estimate the length of his or her toss wins.

Decide

✓ Discuss inches, feet, and yards with your group. How are those units of measure related?

✓ Make a group chart like the one below, and decide the order in which your group members will take turns.

Group Member	Estimate	Toss 1	Toss 2

Do

✓ With your group, use a piece of masking tape to mark a starting line on the floor. With a measuring tape, measure distances of 1, 2, and 3 yards from the starting line. Place a piece of masking tape at each distance.

Starting Line 1 yard 2 yards 3 yards

✓ Have each group member make and record an estimate for the distance he or she thinks a cotton ball can be tossed.

✓ During your turn, stand behind the starting line and toss a cotton ball toward the 3-yard mark. Measure the distance from the starting line to the spot where the cotton ball lands. Record the distance in the chart for Toss 1. After all of your group members have completed and measured Toss 1, do the same for Toss 2.

Share

✓ Display your chart for the class. Did any of your classmates make the same estimates you did?

EP14 Enrich Project

Project Checklist

Evaluate whether each group

_____ engages in a discussion about the relationship between inches, feet, and yards.

_____ cooperatively measures and marks the starting line and each of the three yard lines.

_____ takes turns tossing the cotton balls.

_____ accurately records each toss in the chart.

_____ answers the discussion questions.

_____ compares their chart with those of other groups of students.

SOLUTIONS FOR EXTENSIONS

1a. 130 yards

1b. 340 yards

2a. 16 square units

2b. 6 units

3a. 9; 36

3b. 28

3c. 9

Name____

Extensions

1. A Walk Around the Park

Kayla takes a walk around the park in her neighborhood every day. The park is in the shape of a rectangle. Each time Kayla walks, she begins from the same corner.

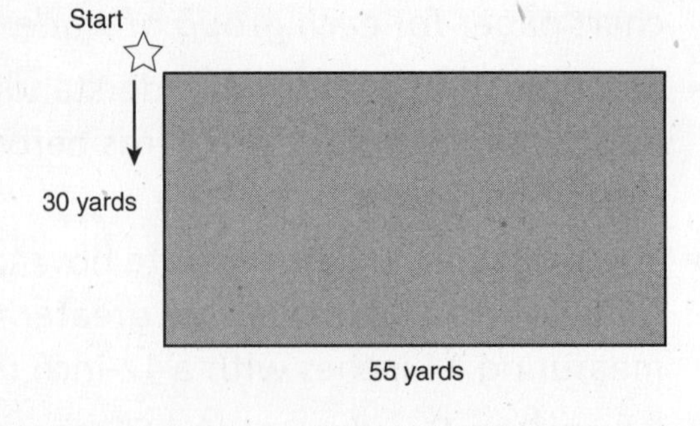

a. On today's walk, Kayla stopped to tie her shoe 40 yards after she started. How far does Kayla have left to walk?

b. Suppose Kayla walks around the park twice. How far will she have walked?

2. Logical Reasoning

Draw a picture to help you solve each problem.

a. Opal drew a square that has an area 4 times the area of Tricia's square. Tricia's square is 2 units wide. What is the area of Opal's square?

b. Tommy's rectangle has a width that is 3 times the width of David's rectangle. David's rectangle is 3 units long and has an area of 6 square units. What is the width of Tommy's rectangle?

3. In Stock

A store clerk is counting the number of boxes of markers he has in stock. The boxes of markers are stacked on the shelf but not all of them can be seen. Each box contains 4 markers.

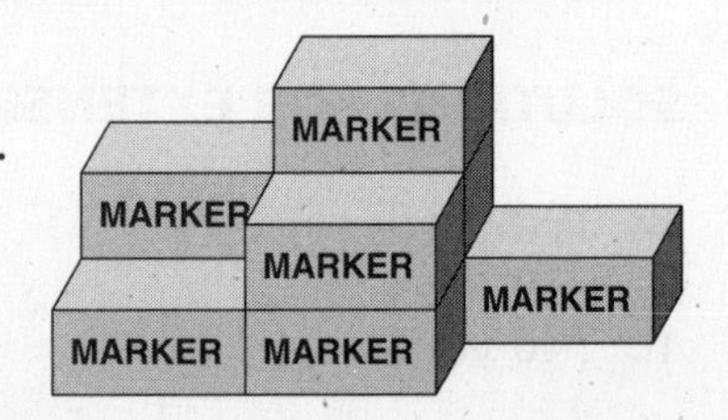

a. How many boxes of markers are on the shelf? How many markers does the clerk have in stock?

b. If the clerk sells two boxes, how many markers will he have left in stock?

c. Suppose the clerk wants to order enough boxes to make the entire stack 3 boxes high, 3 boxes wide, and 2 boxes deep. How many boxes should the clerk order?

TEACHER NOTES FOR PROJECT

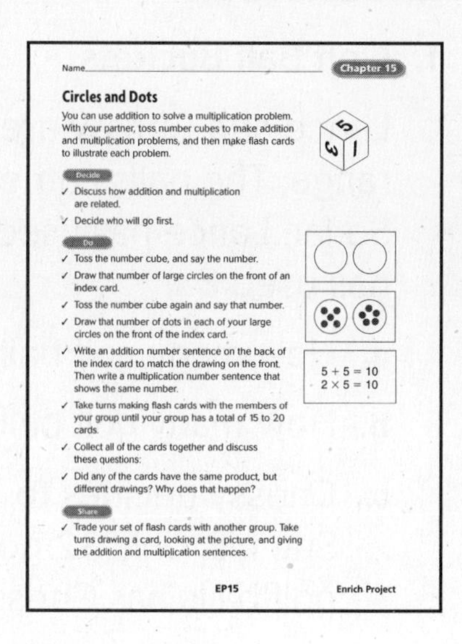

Name__________ Chapter 15

Circles and Dots

You can use addition to solve a multiplication problem. With your partner, toss number cubes to make addition and multiplication problems, and then make flash cards to illustrate each problem.

Decide

- ✓ Discuss how addition and multiplication are related.
- ✓ Decide who will go first.

Do

- ✓ Toss the number cube, and say the number.
- ✓ Draw that number of large circles on the front of an index card.
- ✓ Toss the number cube again and say that number.
- ✓ Draw that number of dots in each of your large circles on the front of the index card.
- ✓ Write an addition number sentence on the back of the index card to match the drawing on the front. Then write a multiplication number sentence that shows the same number.
- ✓ Take turns making flash cards with the members of your group until your group has a total of 15 to 20 cards.
- ✓ Collect all of the cards together and discuss these questions:
- ✓ Did any of the cards have the same product, but different drawings? Why does that happen?

$5 + 5 = 10$
$2 \times 5 = 10$

Share

- ✓ Trade your set of flash cards with another group. Take turns drawing a card, looking at the picture, and giving the addition and multiplication sentences.

EP15 Enrich Project

- **Materials:** number cube labeled 1–6, adequate supply of index cards *for each group of students*
- Review the *Decide*, *Do*, and *Share* steps for completing the project. Answer questions about the steps before the groups begin
their work.
- Be sure students understand that after rolling the second number on the number cube, they are to draw that number of dots inside each circle. Some students may try to divide the second number evenly among the larger circles instead.
- If time allows, have students complete the activity again using a number cube labeled 5–10.

Project Checklist

Evaluate whether each group of students:

_____ uses discussion to review how addition and multiplication are related.

_____ cooperatively decides how the students in the group will take turns.

_____ accurately records each model and represents each model with the correct addition and multiplication sentences.

_____ answers the discussion questions using the flashcards the group has created.

_____ trades flashcards with other groups of students and takes turns giving the correct addition and multiplications sentences.

SOLUTIONS FOR EXTENSIONS

1a. Lance, 300 golf balls; Chrissy, 225 golf balls

1b. 525 golf balls

1c. 257 golf balls

2a. Monday, \$7; Tuesday, \$21; Wednesday, \$63

2b. \$91

3a. 53×8; 424

3b. 58×3; 174

Extensions

1. Golf Ball Buckets

Lance and Chrissy are hitting golf balls at the driving range. The balls come in buckets of 75 golf balls each. So far, Lance has used 4 buckets of golf balls and Chrissy has used 3.

a. How many golf balls have Lance and Chrissy each hit?

b. How many golf balls have they hit altogether?

c. Chrissy decides to get another bucket of golf balls. She hits only 32 golf balls from the bucket. How many golf balls has Chrissy hit in all?

2. Benito's Chores

Benito's grandmother said she would give him $7 to do some chores on Monday. If he did a good job on Monday, she would give him 3 times that much for chores on Tuesday. For Wednesday's chores, she would give him 3 times what he made on Tuesday.

a. How much money does Benito earn each day?

b. How much money would Benito earn altogether for doing chores during the three days?

3. Write the Problem

Jerry wants to use these numbers to write multiplication problems that have a 2-digit factor and a 1-digit factor.

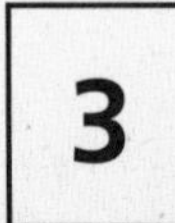

a. What multiplication problem can Jerry write to give him the greatest product possible? What is the product?

b. What multiplication problem can Jerry write to give him the least product possible? What is the product?

TEACHER NOTES FOR PROJECT

- Before beginning the project, have students review basic multiplication facts as well as the multiplication strategies they've learned.
- Students may choose different activities than those listed in the sample table.
- Review the *Decide, Do,* and *Share* steps for completing the project. Answer questions about the stepsbefore the groups begin their work.

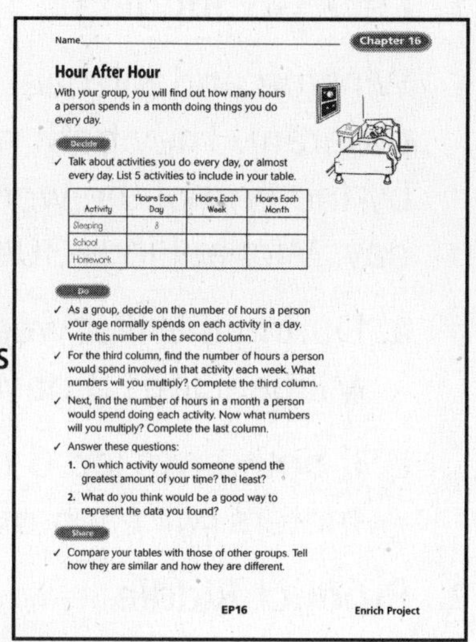
Name________ Chapter 16

Hour After Hour

With your group, you will find out how many hours a person spends in a month doing things you do every day.

Decide

✓ Talk about activities you do every day, or almost every day. List 5 activities to include in your table.

Activity	Hours Each Day	Hours Each Week	Hours Each Month
Sleeping	8		
School			
Homework			

Do

✓ As a group, decide on the number of hours a person your age normally spends on each activity in a day. Write this number in the second column.

✓ For the third column, find the number of hours a person would spend involved in that activity each week. What numbers will you multiply? Complete the third column.

✓ Next, find the number of hours in a month a person would spend doing each activity. Now what numbers will you multiply? Complete the last column.

✓ Answer these questions:

1. On which activity would someone spend the greatest amount of your time? the least?
2. What do you think would be a good way to represent the data you found?

Share

✓ Compare your tables with those of other groups. Tell how they are similar and how they are different.

EP16 Enrich Project

Project Checklist

Evaluate whether each group of students:

______ engages in a discussion about daily activities.

______ creates neatly-written tables to record the data.

______ correctly multiplies the values in the table.

______ compares tables with other groups of students.

SOLUTIONS FOR EXTENSIONS

1a. Winston

1b. Winston, 1,200 meters; Michael, 1,800 meters

2. It felt crummy.

3a. no; $1.47

3b. clock

3c. 3 baskets and a rug

Extensions

1. Let's Go Jogging

Winston and Michael are both starting an exercise program. They both have a goal of jogging 1,000 meters by the end of the week. Winston jogs 200 meters each day. Michael jogs 300 meters each day.

a. During the first week, Winston jogs 5 days and Michael jogs 3 days. Who met the weekly goal?

b. If both boys jog 6 days in the same week, how many meters will each of them jog?

2. Product Riddle

Find each product. Write the letters above the matching products below.

T 4 × 281	**M** 3 × 657	**F** 2 × 409	**M** 7 × 311
Y 9 × 523	**U** 5 × 767	**C** 6 × 138	**L** 8 × 806

Why did the cookie go to the doctor?

I			E		T		R				
___	___	___	___	___	___	___	___	___	___	___	___
	1,124	818		6,448		828		3,835	1,971	2,177	4,707

3. Emma's Dilemma

Emma has $50.00 to spend on either 3 picture frames, 3 pillows, or 3 baskets. With whatever is left over, she will buy either a clock or a rug.

a. Does Emma have enough money to buy 3 pillows and a rug? If yes, tell how much change she will have left over. If no, tell how much more money is needed.

b. Suppose Emma chooses 3 picture frames. Will she have enough to buy the clock or the rug?

c. Which combination of items is more expensive: 3 baskets and a rug, or 3 pillows and a clock?

$12.59 **$10.65** **$11.87**

$17.99

$11.16

TEACHER NOTES FOR PROJECT

- **Materials:** poster board, construction paper, crayons, glue, scissors, and *Divisors* and *Dividends* cards (see Teacher Resource Book) *for each group of students*
- Review the terms *divisor* and *dividend*. Make sure students understand the meaning of each term.
- Discuss the concept of a "remainder." Students should understand that a remainder is the amount left over when a number cannot be divided equally.
- Review the *Decide*, *Do*, and *Share* steps for completing the project. Answer questions about the steps before the groups begin their work

Name____________ Chapter 17

Division Orchard

Apples grow on trees. Oranges grow on trees. Peaches, bananas, and pinecones grow on trees. If you could have a tree that grew anything you wanted, what kind of tree would it be?

Decide

✓ With your group, think of a tree you want to make. Use your imagination! What grows on your imaginary trees? Each member of the group will make his or her own orchard using the group's tree..

Do

✓ Complete this statement: My tree is a ______ tree.

✓ Pick a number card from the stack labeled *Divisors*. This number is the number of trees you will draw in your orchard.

✓ Next, pick a card from the stack labeled *Dividends*. This number is the total number of objects that will grow on the trees in your orchard.

✓ On a piece of poster board, draw the number of trees to represent your divisor. Keep your drawing simple.

✓ Now make the objects to place on your trees. Draw and cut out the correct number of objects to represent your dividend. Divide the objects evenly among all of your trees, and glue them on. If you have any objects left, glue them on the "ground" in your picture.

Share

✓ Share your division orchard with the other members of your group and with your class. Explain how your picture illustrates the divisor and dividend.

EP17 Enrich Project

Project Checklist

Evaluate whether each group of students:

______ works collaboratively to discuss and select different types of trees for their orchards.

______ neatly and correctly displays their divisor and dividend.

______ shares their division orchards with the class.

SOLUTIONS FOR EXTENSIONS

1a. 12 **1b.** 14 **1c.** 5 or 6

2a. A = 8 **2b.** B = 9 **2c.** C = 3

3a. medium baskets **3b.** 14; 4

Extensions

1. You're the Boss

Suppose you are in charge of a toy company. Each day your company builds 48 robots and delivers an equal number to four different toy stores.

a. How many robots does each toy store receive?

b. If you were to increase your production rate to 56 robots each day, how many robots would each of the four stores receive?

c. You decide that you want to deliver to more stores, either 5, 6, or 7. You want each store to receive at least 12 robots. If your company makes 78 robots each day, how many stores can you deliver to?

2. Find the Missing Digits

Each letter below stands for a digit. Find digits that will make each number sentence true.

a. 4A ÷ 8 = 4 **b.** 83 ÷ B = B r2 **c.** CC ÷ 8 = 4 r1

3. Apple Baskets

A farmer puts all the apples he picks into baskets to be sold at a produce market. Small baskets will hold 5 apples, medium baskets will hold 7 apples, and large baskets will hold 9 apples. The farmer has picked 154 apples to fill the baskets.

a. The farmer wants to sell all of his apples. Which size baskets should he use so that there are no apples left over?

b. Suppose the farmer wants to use some of each size basket. If he uses 5 medium baskets and 5 large baskets, how many small baskets could he fill with the rest of the apples? How many apples would be left over?

TEACHER NOTES FOR PROJECT

- **Materials:** pattern blocks *for each pair of students*
- Students should have an understanding of basic fractions before beginning the *Do* step of the project.
- Before students begin, you may wish to review how to write a fraction to represent part of a whole.
- Review the *Decide*, *Do*, and *Share* steps for completing the project. Answer questions about the steps before the groups begin their work.

Name ______________________ Chapter 18

Fraction Cover-Up

Work with a partner to model parts of wholes by using pattern blocks.

Decide

✓ Each of you will model two problems in the table below. The other will write a conclusion based on what you find out. Decide who will model first.

Pattern Block Equal to 1	Block to Use to Cover	Number of Blocks Used	Conclusion
		2	is $\frac{1}{2}$ of

Do

✓ For each pair of pattern blocks shown in the table, use as many smaller pattern blocks as it takes to cover the larger pattern block. Record the number of blocks you used.

✓ Write a conclusion using a fraction to describe what part the smaller pattern block is of the larger block.

Share

✓ Share completed tables with other pairs of students. Did they reach the same conclusions as you?

EP18 Enrich Project

Project Checklist

Evaluate whether each pair of students:

_____ cooperatively decides how they will take turns.

_____ uses the pattern blocks to accurately model each problem.

_____ accurately records the data in the table and writes a conclusion to represent the results.

_____ compares their table with those of other students.

SOLUTIONS FOR EXTENSIONS

1a.

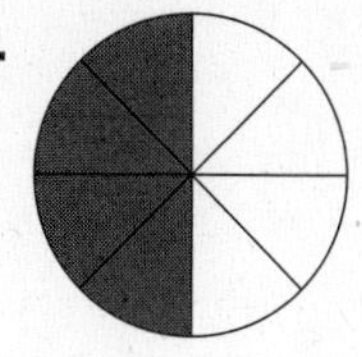

1b.

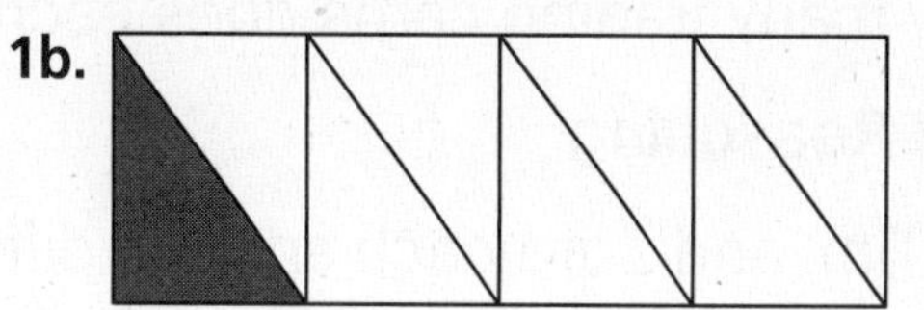

2a. Evan and Chloe

2b. Gary, 6; Evan, 3; Chloe, 3

3. Jenny, $\frac{1}{2}$ hour; Tim, $\frac{4}{10}$ hour; Zora, $\frac{3}{5}$ hour

Name____ Chapter 18

Extensions

1. Shady Figures

An ***analogy*** is a comparison between two pairs of things. It is written to show the relationship between the objects in each pair.

For example:

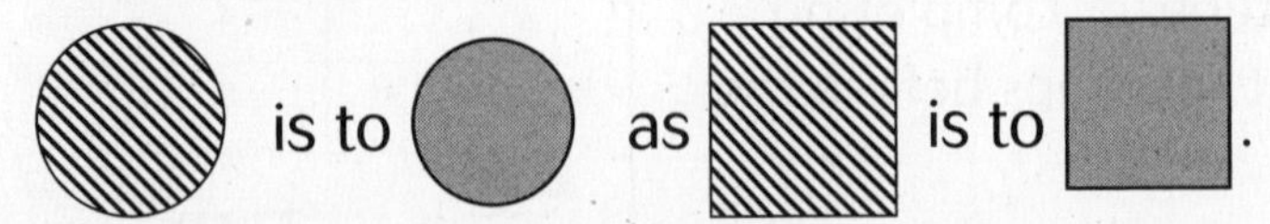

Shade the last figure in each analogy.

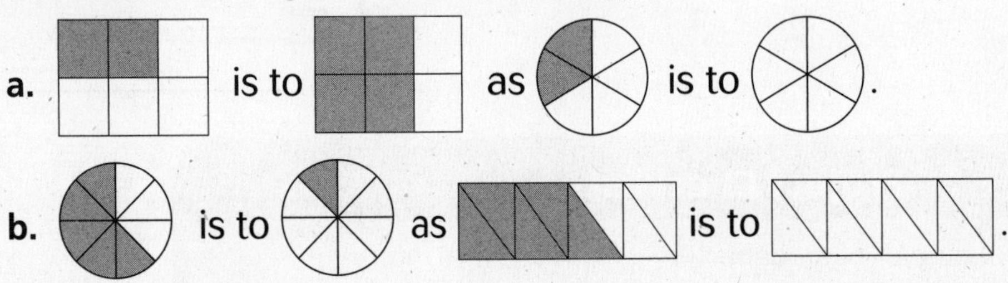

2. Trading Cards

Gary, Evan, and Chloe have a total of 12 trading cards. Gary has $\frac{1}{2}$ of the trading cards. Evan has $\frac{3}{12}$ of the trading cards and Chloe has $\frac{1}{4}$ of the trading cards.

a. Which two people have the same number of trading cards?

b. How many trading cards does each person have?

3. Logical Reasoning

Jenny, Tim, and Zora each spent a different amount of time completing homework. The amounts of time are $\frac{1}{2}$ hour, $\frac{4}{10}$ hour, and $\frac{3}{5}$ hour. Tim spent the least amount of time on homework. Jenny spent more time than Tim but less time than Zora. How long did each person spend on homework?

TEACHER NOTES FOR PROJECT

- Before beginning the project, have students review basic multiplication facts as well as the multiplication strategies they've learned.
- Students may choose different activities than those listed in the sample table.
- Review the *Decide*, *Do*, and *Share* steps for completing the project. Answer questions about the steps before the groups begin their work.

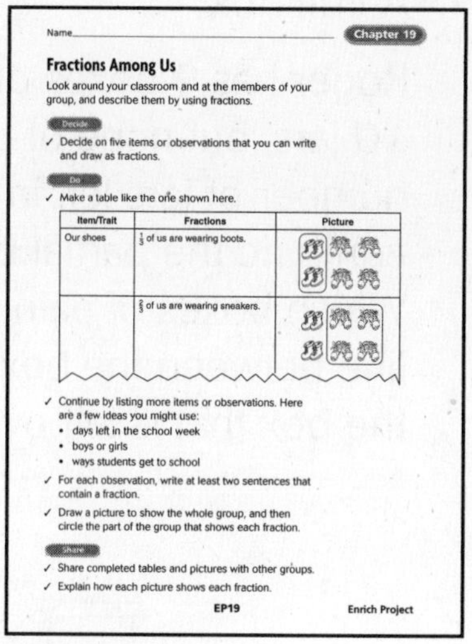

Name______________________ Chapter 19

Fractions Among Us

Look around your classroom and at the members of your group, and describe them by using fractions.

Decide

✓ Decide on five items or observations that you can write and draw as fractions.

Do

✓ Make a table like the one shown here.

Item/Trait	Fractions	Picture
Our shoes	$\frac{1}{3}$ of us are wearing boots.	
	$\frac{2}{3}$ of us are wearing sneakers.	

✓ Continue by listing more items or observations. Here are a few ideas you might use:
- days left in the school week
- boys or girls
- ways students get to school

✓ For each observation, write at least two sentences that contain a fraction.

✓ Draw a picture to show the whole group, and then circle the part of the group that shows each fraction.

Share

✓ Share completed tables and pictures with other groups.

✓ Explain how each picture shows each fraction.

EP19 Enrich Project

Project Checklist

Evaluate whether each group

______ cooperatively decides which 5 items or observations will be used for the project.

______ creates a neatly-written table to record the sentences and fraction models.

______ accurately writes fractions that represent the models drawn.

______ shares completed tables with other groups of students.

SOLUTIONS FOR EXTENSIONS

1. $\frac{7}{10}$, $\frac{4}{10}$, $\frac{5}{10}$, $\frac{5}{10}$, $\frac{8}{10}$, $\frac{9}{10}$, $\frac{6}{10}$, $\frac{3}{10}$, $\frac{2}{10}$

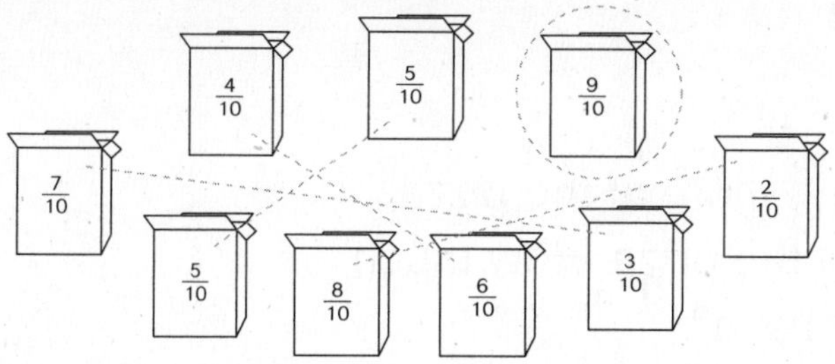

2a. $\frac{2}{5} + \frac{1}{5} = \frac{3}{5}$

2b. $\frac{5}{5} - \frac{3}{5} = \frac{2}{5}$

3a. Chad, $\frac{5}{8}$; Lenny, $\frac{1}{8}$

3b. Tanya, $\frac{4}{12}$; Lora, $\frac{5}{12}$; $\frac{1}{12}$

Name____

Extensions

1. A Full Box

Roger has 9 boxes of paints. Each box of paints holds 10 jars, but none of the boxes are full. Roger wrote the number of jars left in the box as a fraction. He wants to combine the partial boxes of paints to make 4 full boxes. Which boxes of paints should Roger combine? Draw a line between the boxes that should be combined. Circle the box that is left over.

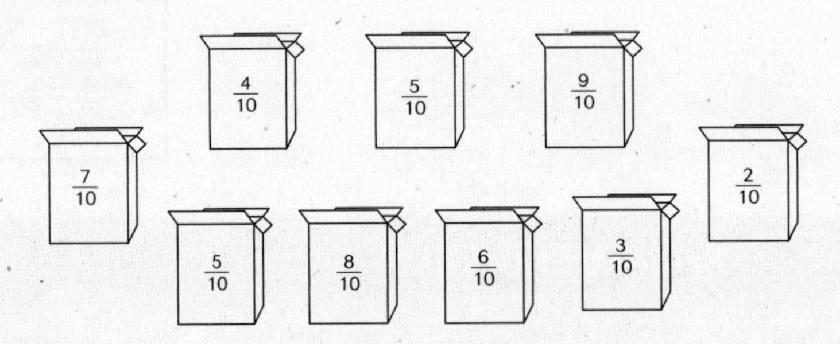

2. Dwight's Day

Write a number sentence for each question using fractions.

Dwight spent two fifths of an hour doing his homework and one fifth of an hour having a snack.

a. How much time did Dwight spend on his homework and having a snack?

b. How much of the hour was left after Dwight completed his homework and had a snack?

3. Logical Reasoning

a. Sheryl ate $\frac{2}{8}$ of a pizza. Chad ate $\frac{3}{8}$ more of the pizza than Sheryl. Lenny ate the rest of the pizza. How much of the pizza did Chad and Lenny have?

b. Some friends are sharing a bag of grapes. Tanya has 2 times the amount of grapes that Jolie has. Lora has $\frac{1}{12}$ more of the bag than Tanya. If Jolie has $\frac{2}{12}$ of the bag, what fraction of the grapes do Tanya and Lora have? What fraction of the grapes are left in the bag?

TEACHER NOTES FOR PROJECT

- **Materials:** sticky notes and index cards *for each pair of students*
- Students should be able to add and subtract money with regrouping before beginning the *Do* step of the project.
- Remind students to price each item in their desks at an amount that is less than $2.50.
- Review the *Decide, Do,* and *Share* steps for completing the project. Answer questions about the steps before the groups begin their work.

Name______________ Chapter 20

School Supply Sale

You and your partner will practice selling and buying school supplies you find in and around your desks.

Decide

✓ Work with your partner to select ten items of school supplies from in and around your desks that you will sell.

✓ Discuss how to add and subtract money amounts.

✓ Decide who will be the seller first, and who will be the buyer.

Do

✓ Collect ten items of school supplies on your desk. Some of them can be duplicates. Use sticky notes to label each item with a price less than $2.50.

✓ The buyer selects two items that he or she wants to buy, and tells the seller.

✓ The seller makes a receipt on an index card by writing the items and their prices. The seller then adds the prices to find the total sale amount.

School Supply Receipt	
pen	$0.79
stapler	$2.49
TOTAL:	
CHANGE:	

✓ The seller then calculates the amount of change due the buyer if he or she had paid for the items with a $5.00 bill.

✓ Once the receipt is complete, switch roles. Repeat this until you and your partner each have had a chance to shop five times.

✓ When you each have completed all of your shopping, discuss these questions:

1. Which pair of items cost the most? Which pair cost the least?
2. Pick any receipt. How could the seller have made change using only $1.00 bills, dimes, and pennies?

Share

✓ Invite other pairs to shop from your desk. Find how much it would cost to buy two items from their desks.

EP20 Enrich Project

Project Checklist

Evaluate whether each pair of students:

_____ cooperatively decides how they will take turns.

_____ selects and then labels items with a price of $2.50 or less.

_____ accurately adds and subtracts the amounts on each receipt.

_____ answers the discussion questions using the values on the receipts.

_____ practices buying and selling items with other pairs of students.

SOLUTIONS FOR EXTENSIONS

1a. $\frac{1}{10}$ **1b.** 0.4

1c. stars **1d.** 0.5

2. Card A, 1.23; Card B, 5.4; Card C, 1.09; Card D, 6.8

3a. 3 nickels, 4 quarters, 3 pennies

3b. $1.18; $0.15 + $1.00 + $0.03 = $1.18

Name____

Extensions

1. Shelly's Tiles

Shelly has a box of square tiles. Each square tile is painted with a different figure.

a. What fraction of the tiles have a heart?

b. Write a decimal that shows the number of tiles with a circle.

c. Which figure represents 0.3 of the tiles?

d. Suppose Shelly traded all the star tiles for triangle tiles. Write a decimal to represent the number of triangles tiles Shelly would have.

2. Missing Digits

Tina wrote some decimal numbers on index cards. She covered some of the digits on each card. Use the clues to complete the numbers on each card.

- The missing digit on Card B is 1 less than the ones digit on Card D.
- The missing digit on Card A is the sum of the digit in the ones place and the digit in the tenths place.
- The missing digit in the hundredths place on Card C is 3 times the hundredths digit in Card A.
- The missing digit in the ones place on Card C is the difference of the digit in the ones place and the digit in the tenths place on Card B.
- The missing digit on Card D is 3 greater than the digit in the ones place on Card B.

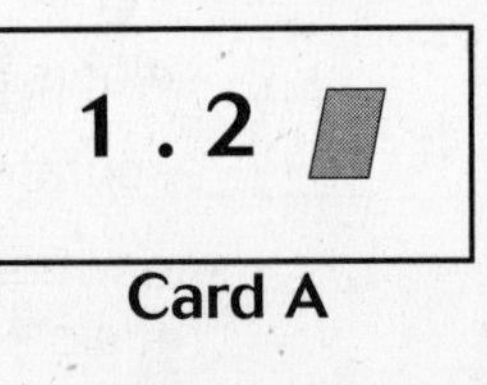

Card A

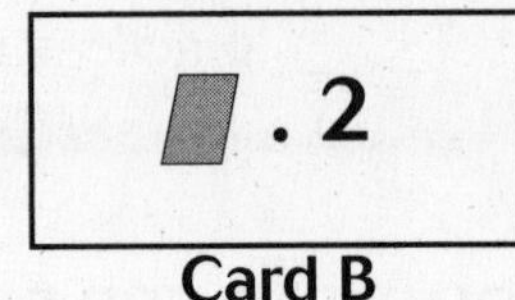

Card B

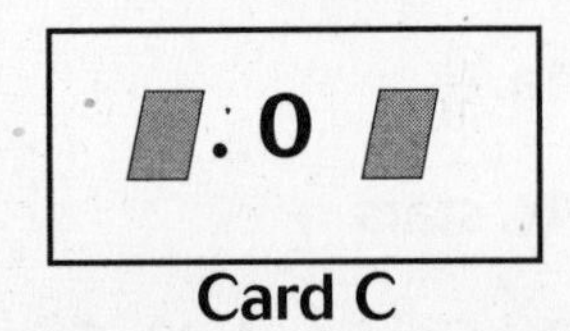

Card C

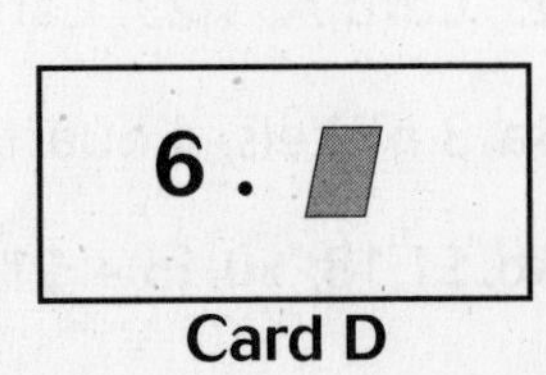

Card D

3. A Money Problem

Toshiro has 10 coins. $\frac{3}{10}$ of the coins are nickels and 0.4 of the coins are quarters. The rest of the coins are pennies.

a. How many of each coin does Toshiro have?

b. How much money does Toshiro have in all?

TEACHER NOTES FOR PROJECT

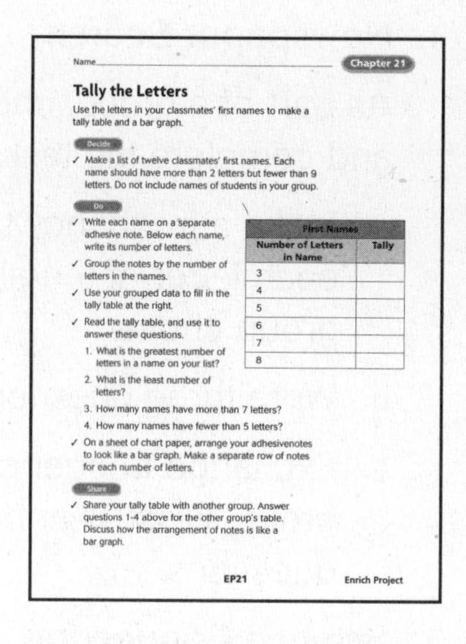

Name__________ Chapter 21

Tally the Letters

Use the letters in your classmates' first names to make a tally table and a bar graph.

Decide

✓ Make a list of twelve classmates' first names. Each name should have more than 2 letters but fewer than 9 letters. Do not include names of students in your group.

Do

✓ Write each name on a separate adhesive note. Below each name, write its number of letters.

✓ Group the notes by the number of letters in the names.

✓ Use your grouped data to fill in the tally table at the right.

✓ Read the tally table, and use it to answer these questions.

1. What is the greatest number of letters in a name on your list?
2. What is the least number of letters?
3. How many names have more than 7 letters?
4. How many names have fewer than 5 letters?

✓ On a sheet of chart paper, arrange your adhesivenotes to look like a bar graph. Make a separate row of notes for each number of letters.

First Names	
Number of Letters in Name	Tally
3	
4	
5	
6	
7	
8	

Share

✓ Share your tally table with another group. Answer questions 1-4 above for the other group's table. Discuss how the arrangement of notes is like a bar graph.

EP21 Enrich Project

- **Materials:** 15 adhesive notes (1″ × 2″ up to 3″ × 5″), chart paper *for each group*
- Tell students to leave the Tally column blank next to numbers of letters for which they have no names.
- Some groups may need guidance when arranging the adhesive notes to look like a bar graph. Make sure they understand that the notes should be adjacent, not stacked or overlapping.
- Tell students to leave a blank row in the bar graph to correspond to any row without tally marks in the table.
- As an alternative, groups may arrange the notes in columns to make a vertical bar graph rather than a horizontal graph.
- Review the *Decide*, *Do*, and *Share* steps for completing the project. Answer questions about the steps before the groups begin their work.

Project Checklist

Evaluate whether each group

_____ cooperatively makes a list of 12 classmates' first names.

_____ writes each name and the number of letters in it on a separate adhesive note.

_____ groups the notes according to the numbers of letters in the names.

_____ completes the tally table.

_____ arranges the adhesive notes to look like a bar graph.

_____ exchanges tally tables with another group and uses the new table to answer the questions.

SOLUTIONS FOR EXTENSIONS

1. Frequency tables and questions will vary.
2. Check students' work.
3.

Volcanoes			
	8,000–9,999 feet	10,000–11,999 feet	Greater than 12,000 feet
California		1	1
Oregon	1	2	
Washington	1	2	2

Name________________________________

Extensions

1. Newspaper Search

As part of a group, choose a paragraph in a newspaper and complete the tasks below.

a. Make a frequency table to show the number of each letter of the alphabet in the paragraph your group chose.

b. Write three questions about the frequency table.

c. Exchange frequency tables and questions with another group. Discuss and answer the other group's questions.

2. Science Connection

Use reference books to find the top speeds (in miles per hour) of four different animals.

a. Make a bar graph to show the speeds of the animals you chose.

b. Compare your bar graph with a classmate's graph. Discuss what makes some animals faster than others.

3. Classify Volcanoes

Linda made the list at the right. Use her list to make a table that tallies the volcanoes by location and height. List states on the left side of the table, and label the other columns with the following height categories:

- 8,000–9,999 feet
- 10,000–11,999 feet
- greater than 12,000 feet

Heights of Volcanoes
Mount Bailey, Oregon: 8,368 feet
Glacier Peak, Washington: 10,541 feet
Lassen Peak, California: 10,457 feet
Mount Adams, Washington: 12,276 feet
Mount Baker, Washington: 10,781 feet
Mount Hood, Oregon: 11,240 feet
Mount Jefferson, Oregon: 10,513 feet
Mount. Rainier, Washington: 14,410 feet
Mount St. Helens, Washington: 8,364 feet
Mount Shasta, California: 14,162 feet

Chapter 22

TEACHER NOTES FOR PROJECT

- **Materials:** chart paper, rulers *for each group*
- Answers to bulleted questions:
  The activities offered on Thursday are Family Film Hour, Book Talk, Read-Aloud Time, and Meet the Author. The most activities are scheduled on Friday.
- Review the *Decide*, *Do*, and *Share* steps for completing the project. Answer questions about the steps before the groups begin their work.
- Students' codes may differ. A sample completed table is shown below.

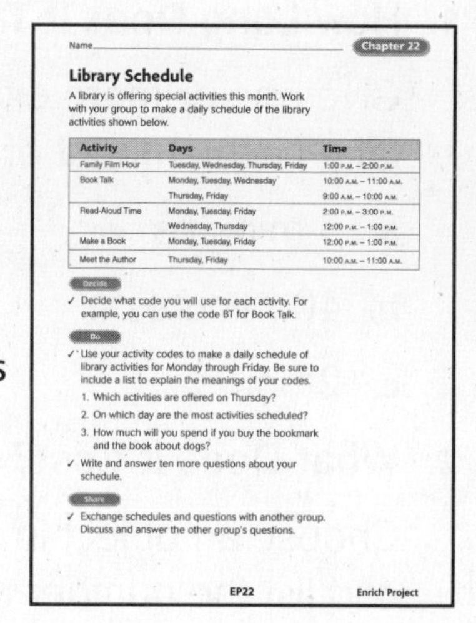

Name__________ Chapter 22

Library Schedule

A library is offering special activities this month. Work with your group to make a daily schedule of the library activities shown below.

Activity	Days	Time
Family Film Hour	Tuesday, Wednesday, Thursday, Friday	1:00 P.M. – 2:00 P.M.
Book Talk	Monday, Tuesday, Wednesday	10:00 A.M. – 11:00 A.M.
	Thursday, Friday	9:00 A.M. – 10:00 A.M.
Read-Aloud Time	Monday, Tuesday, Friday	2:00 P.M. – 3:00 P.M.
	Wednesday, Thursday	12:00 P.M. – 1:00 P.M.
Make a Book	Monday, Tuesday, Friday	12:00 P.M. – 1:00 P.M.
Meet the Author	Thursday, Friday	10:00 A.M. – 11:00 A.M.

Decide

✓ Decide what code you will use for each activity. For example, you can use the code BT for Book Talk.

Do

✓ Use your activity codes to make a daily schedule of library activities for Monday through Friday. Be sure to include a list to explain the meanings of your codes.

1. Which activities are offered on Thursday?
2. On which day are the most activities scheduled?
3. How much will you spend if you buy the bookmark and the book about dogs?

✓ Write and answer ten more questions about your schedule.

Share

✓ Exchange schedules and questions with another group. Discuss and answer the other group's questions.

EP22 Enrich Project

	Monday	Tuesday	Wednesday	Thursday	Friday
9:00 – 10:00				BT	BT
10:00 – 11:00	BT	BT	BT	MA	MA
11:00 – 12:00					
12:00 – 1:00	MB	MB	RAT	RAT	MB
1:00 – 2:00		FF	FF	FF	FF
2:00 – 3:00	RAT	RAT			RAT

Project Checklist

Evaluate whether each group

_____ cooperatively chooses a code to represent each activity.

_____ neatly and accurately makes a daily schedule for the library activities.

_____ answers the two bulleted questions in the *Decide* step.

_____ writes ten more questions that can be answered by using its schedule.

_____ exchanges schedules with another group and participates in group discussion.

SOLUTIONS FOR EXTENSIONS

1. Answers will vary. Possible answers:
   1a. get dressed for school **1b.** do homework **1c.** watch a movie
2. Check students' work.
3. Check students' work.

Extensions

1. How Long Does It Take?

Give one or more examples of an activity that could take each amount of time listed below.

a. 5 minutes

b. 40 minutes

c. 2 hours

2. What Does It Cost?

Choose an object in the classroom, estimate its value, and list the number and types of bills and coins that can be used to make that money amount. Share and discuss your estimates and lists with the other members of your group.

3. Different Kinds of Clocks

Three different kinds of clocks and timers from the past are sundials, hourglasses, and water clocks. Look up each kind of clock in an encyclopedia. Write an explanation of how each works.

4. Plan for Buying Tickets

The ticket prices for an amusement park are listed below. Suppose you won a $50.00 gift certificate for the park. Would this amount be enough to buy tickets for all members of your family? Show your work.

Children (ages 2 and under)	FREE
Children (ages 3–12)	$ 9.95
Teenagers and Adults	$15.95
Seniors (ages 55–69)	$ 9.95
Honorary Seniors (70+)	FREE

TEACHER NOTES FOR PROJECT

- **Materials:** poster board, 4 colors of yarn, markers, scissors, and glue *for each group of students*
- Students should have a basic understanding of the measurements of inch, foot, and yard before beginning the *Do* step of the project.
- Remind students of proper safety when using scissors.
- Suggest that group members work together to measure and mark the yarn.
- Review the *Decide*, *Do*, and Share steps for completing the project. Answer questions about the steps before the groups begin their work.

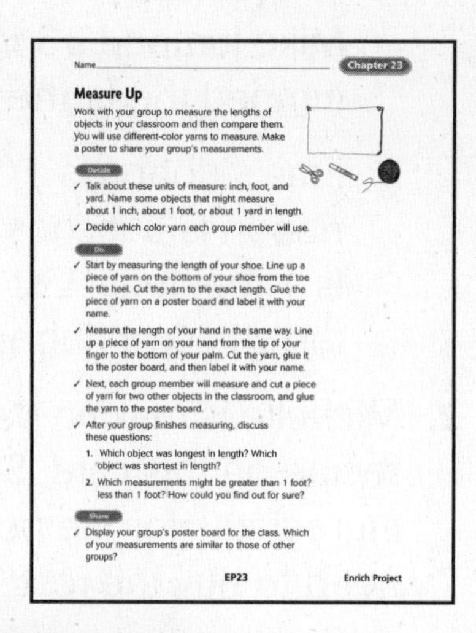

Name________________ Chapter 23

Measure Up

Work with your group to measure the lengths of objects in your classroom and then compare them. You will use different-color yarns to measure. Make a poster to share your group's measurements.

Decide

✓ Talk about these units of measure: inch, foot, and yard. Name some objects that might measure about 1 inch, about 1 foot, or about 1 yard in length.

✓ Decide which color yarn each group member will use.

Do

✓ Start by measuring the length of your shoe. Line up a piece of yarn on the bottom of your shoe from the toe to the heel. Cut the yarn to the exact length. Glue the piece of yarn on a poster board and label it with your name.

✓ Measure the length of your hand in the same way. Line up a piece of yarn on your hand from the tip of your finger to the bottom of your palm. Cut the yarn, glue it to the poster board, and then label it with your name.

✓ Next, each group member will measure and cut a piece of yarn for two other objects in the classroom, and glue the yarn to the poster board.

✓ After your group finishes measuring, discuss these questions:

1. Which object was longest in length? Which object was shortest in length?
2. Which measurements might be greater than 1 foot? less than 1 foot? How could you find out for sure?

Share

✓ Display your group's poster board for the class. Which of your measurements are similar to those of other groups?

EP23 Enrich Project

Project Checklist

Evaluate whether each group of students:

_____ engages in a discussion about the terms inch, foot, and yard.

_____ cooperatively selects a yarn color for each group member.

_____ accurately measures, marks, and cuts each piece of yarn.

_____ glues and labels each piece of yarn neatly on the poster board.

_____ answers the discussion questions.

_____ compares the group's measurements with those of other groups.

SOLUTIONS FOR EXTENSIONS

1a. Greg **1b.** Gina, Leslie, Fran

2a. Possible answer: Michelle has enough cranberry juice but not enough orange juice to make the punch.

2b. 4 cans

2c. orange juice = 2 quarts, 1 pint; cranberry juice = 1 quart; lemon-lime soda = 1 gallon; pineapple juice = 1 pint

3. Possible answer: Brad should take 4 ounces of peanuts out of the scale in the middle, add 6 ounces of peanuts to the scale on the left, and add 3 ounces of peanuts to the scale on the right.

Name____

Extensions

1. Logical Reasoning

a. In a jumping contest, Greg jumped 2 feet 13 inches. Mike jumped 33 inches. Ricardo jumped 1 yard. Who jumped the farthest?

b. Fran's ribbon is 10 inches longer than Gina's. Gina's ribbon is 5 inches shorter than Leslie's. Leslie's ribbon is 1 foot long. List the names of the girls in order from the shortest ribbon to the longest ribbon.

2. Michelle is making party punch by using the recipe on this card. She has some of the ingredients for the punch already, but will need to buy the rest.

Party Punch Recipe (makes 1 gallon)	
Orange juice	5 cups
Cranberry juice	1 pint
Lemon-lime soda	2 quarts
Pineapple juice	1 cup

a. Michelle already has 1 quart of orange juice and 3 cups of cranberry juice in the refrigerator. Does she have enough of each kind of juice to make the punch?

b. Michelle will buy the lemon-lime soda in cans. Each can is about 2 cups. How many cans will Michelle need to buy?

c. Suppose Michelle wants to double the recipe. How much of each ingredient will Michelle need? Rewrite the amount of each ingredient using the largest unit of measure possible.

3. A Pound of Peanuts

Brad is dividing 3 pounds of peanuts into three cups. He wants each cup to hold 1 pound of peanuts.

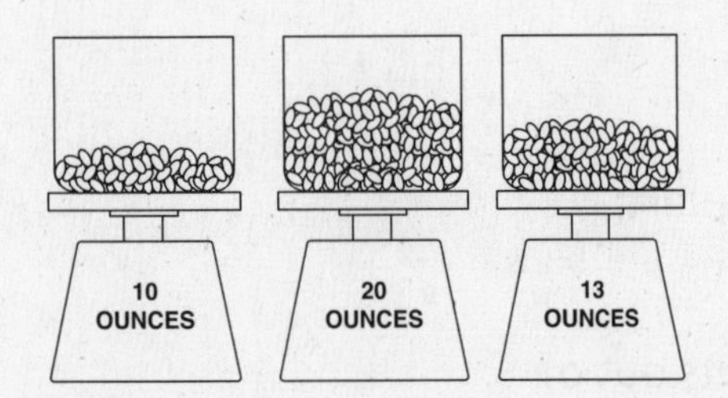

Brad put some of the peanuts in the cups. He has 5 ounces of peanuts left in his hand. What should Brad do to make each cup of peanuts equal 1 pound?

TEACHER NOTES FOR PROJECT

- **Materials:** chart paper *for each pair of students*
- Students should have a basic understanding of the measurements of centimeter and meter before beginning the *Do* step of the project.
- Review the *Decide, Do,* and *Share* steps for completing the project. Answer questions before the groups begin their work.
- If time allows, have students measure some of the objects using yarn or string to verify the lengths. Have them glue the yarn to the chart paper and label each piece with the name of the object that was measured.

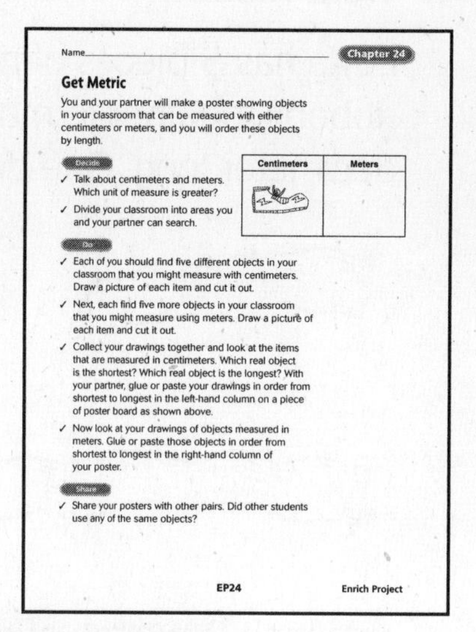

Name____________________ Chapter 24

Get Metric

You and your partner will make a poster showing objects in your classroom that can be measured with either centimeters or meters, and you will order these objects by length.

Decide

✓ Talk about centimeters and meters. Which unit of measure is greater?

✓ Divide your classroom into areas you and your partner can search.

Centimeters	Meters

Do

✓ Each of you should find five different objects in your classroom that you might measure with centimeters. Draw a picture of each item and cut it out.

✓ Next, each find five more objects in your classroom that you might measure using meters. Draw a picture of each item and cut it out.

✓ Collect your drawings together and look at the items that are measured in centimeters. Which real object is the shortest? Which real object is the longest? With your partner, glue or paste your drawings in order from shortest to longest in the left-hand column on a piece of poster board as shown above.

✓ Now look at your drawings of objects measured in meters. Glue or paste those objects in order from shortest to longest in the right-hand column of your poster.

Share

✓ Share your posters with other pairs. Did other students use any of the same objects?

EP24 Enrich Project

Project Checklist

Evaluate whether each group of students:

______ engages in a discussion about the terms centimeter and meter.

______ works together to identify objects in the room that might be measured with centimeters or meters.

______ cooperatively decides how to number the objects from shortest to longest.

______ neatly rewrites the list of objects on the chart paper for display.

______ compares their chart with those of other students.

SOLUTIONS FOR EXTENSIONS

1a. 1 centimeter, 3 centimeters, 6 centimeters

1b. 5 centimeter, 6 centimeters, 8 centimeters; 9 centimeters longer

2a. 400 milliliters

2b. 350 milliliters

2c. Sasha; 50 milliliters

3a. Lucy, 575 grams; Kwan, 375 grams

3b. 1,150 grams; more

Name____

Extensions

1. Tie a Ribbon

Leyla has 5 pieces of ribbon. She wants to put 3 short ribbons together to make a long ribbon that is one decimeter long. One decimeter is equal to 10 centimeters.

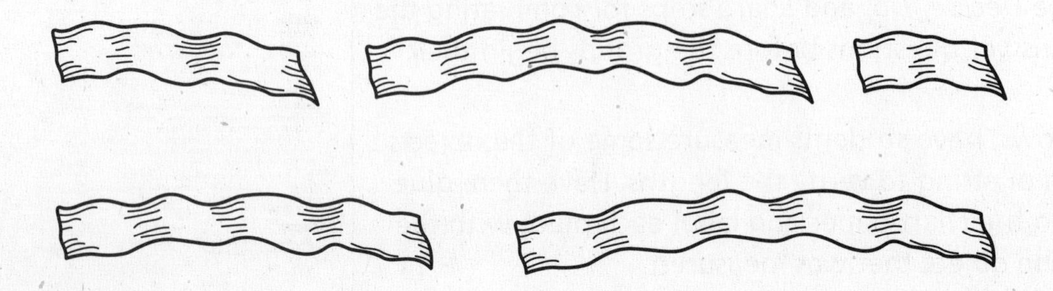

a. Which 3 pieces of ribbon should Leyla put together?

b. Suppose Leyla wants the longest ribbon possible. Which 3 pieces should she put together? How much longer than a one decimeter will the ribbon be?

2. Milliliters of Milk

Marcus adopted two young kittens, Rusty and Sasha. The kittens drink a special kind of milk that Marcus got from the veterinarian. Marcus got 1 liter of milk for each kitten at the beginning of the week.

a. Rusty drank 200 milliliters a day for the first 3 days. How much of his 1 liter of milk is left?

b. Sasha drank 270 milliliters the first day and 190 milliliters each day for the next 2 days. How much of her 1 liter of milk is left?

c. Which kitten drank more milk in the first 3 days? How much more?

3. A Popcorn Problem

Dan has 250 grams of popcorn. Lucy has 275 grams more popcorn than Dan. Kwan has 150 grams less than Lucy.

a. How much popcorn do Lucy and Kwan have?

b. How much popcorn do Dan, Lucy, and Kwan have in all? Is it more or less than 1 kilogram?

Enrich Worksheets

Name________________

Number Pattern Riddles

To solve each riddle, follow the instructions in each exercise to mark the numbers in the hundred chart below. You will have to mark some numbers more than once.

1	2	3	4	5	6	7	8	9	10
11	12	13	14	15	16	17	18	19	20
21	22	23	24	25	26	27	28	29	30
31	32	33	34	35	36	37	38	39	40
41	42	43	44	45	46	47	48	49	50
51	52	53	54	55	56	57	58	59	60
61	62	63	64	65	66	67	68	69	70
71	72	73	74	75	76	77	78	79	80
81	82	83	84	85	86	87	88	89	90
91	92	93	94	95	96	97	98	99	100

1. We are numbers whose digits are equal. What numbers are we? Mark us with a diagonal line on the hundred chart.
   11, 22, 33, 44, 55, 66, 77, 88, 99
2. We are numbers whose digits have a sum of 12. What numbers are we? Mark us with a diagonal line on the hundred chart.
   39, 48, 57, 66, 75, 84, 93
3. We are numbers whose ones digit is less than 1. What numbers are we? Mark us with a vertical line on the hundred chart.
   10, 20, 30, 40, 50, 60, 70, 80, 90, 100
4. We are numbers whose tens digit minus the ones digit is 2. What numbers are we? Mark us with a diagonal line on the hundred chart.
   31, 42, 53, 64, 75, 86, 97

Think About It!

5. WRITE Math Explain how you found the answer to exercise 4?
   Possible Answer; I started in the 90s figuring out that 9 – 7 = 5, then I just followed a backward diagonal line checking my answers for accuracy along the way.

Name________________

3-Digit Place Value Riddle

Locate the place value in the table below of each underlined digit, in each exercise.

1 A	2 B	3 C	4 D	5 E	6 F	7 G	8 H	9 I
10 J	20 K	30 L	40 M	50 N	60 O	70 P	80 Q	90 R
100 S	200 T	300 U	400 V	500 W	600 X	700 Y	800 Z	900 AA

1. 901
2. 91
3. 44
4. 444
5. 101
6. 999
7. 123
8. 1
9. 11
10. 99
11. 654
12. 505
13. 262
14. 30
15. 966

Use your answers to solve the riddle.

What are the first two animals found in the dictionary?

AA (1) **R** (2) **D** (3) **V** (4) **A** (5) **R** (6) **K** (7)

and

A (8) **A** (9) **R** (10) **D** (11) **W** (12) **O** (13) **L** (14) **F** (15)

Name________

Place Value Treasure Chest

The combination to a locked treasure chest is a 4-digit code. The missing numbers in exercises 1–6 provide clues to help you find the combination. Find the missing numbers?

1. 3,000 + **50** + 9 = 3,059
2. **1,000** + 300 + 60 + 5 = 1,365
3. 4,000 + 600 + **70** = 4,670
4. 2,000 + 800 + **4** = 2,804
5. **7,000** + 2 = 7,002
6. 4,000 + **200** + 90 + 2 = 4,292

7. To find the 4-digit code, add your answers from exercises 1–6. What is the combination to the locked treasure chest?

8 **3** **2** **4**

Think About It!

8. **Stretch Your Thinking** You open the treasure chest, but instead of treasure there's another lock and a note with a riddle on it! Use your combination from exercise 7 and the place value riddle below to open the new lock.

Your thousands is my hundreds, your hundreds is my ones. Your tens is my thousands, and your ones is my tens. What 4-digit number am I?

2 **8** **4** **3**

In case student got wrong answer for #7, instructor may check accuracy of riddle solution using whatever 4-digit answer student gave for #7.

Name________

Scrambled Place Values

Arrange the numbers from each circle to make your own 5-digit number. Write the standard form and the expanded form of your number on the lines under the circle.

1. 1 4 7 6 0

Answers will vary. Check for accuracy.

2. 9 1 3 5 8

Answers will vary. Check for accuracy.

3. 4 8 2 1 3

Answers will vary. Check for accuracy.

4. 5 9 0 2 7

Answers will vary. Check for accuracy.

Think About It!

5. **Stretch Your Thinking** Use the place value chart below to show the least number you can make using all the numbers in the circle from exercise 4.

ten thousands	thousands	hundreds	tens	ones
2	0	5	7	9

6. WRITE Math Explain how you found the answer to exercise 5.

I placed the smallest numbers in the highest place value positions except for 0 since a number may not begin ith 0. ***If student missed #5, check explanation in #6 for understanding of place value.***

Name________________ Lesson 1.5

When Is My Party?

Darcy, Rory, Anita, and Lindsey all wanted to have a party in May. Each of them wanted their party on a different date. Use the calendar and the clues to find when each person's party will be.

MAY

Sun	Mon	Tues	Wed	Thurs	Fri	Sat
		1	2	3	4	5
6	7	8	9	10	11	12
13	14	15	16	17	18	19
20	21	22	23	24	25	26
27	28	29	30	31		

1. Darcy's party is on a date with 2 odd digits, and with digits that have a sum of 6. When is Darcy's party?

   May 15th

2. Rory's party is on an odd-numbered date. The digits of this date have a sum of 2 and a difference of 0. When is Rory's party?

   May 11th

3. Anita's party is on a date between the 14th and the 25th. The sum of this date's digits is 5. When is Anita's party?

   May 23rd

4. Lindsey's party is before the 28th, on a date with a ones digit that is greater than its tens digit. If you subtract 7 from its ones digit, the difference is its tens digit. When is Lindsey's party?

   May 18th

Think About It!

5. WRITE Math Explain the steps you used to determine Lindsey's party in exercise 4.

[Order of steps may vary.] I crossed out all the one-digit dates. I crossed out dates higher than 28. I crossed dates whose ones digit was smaller than the tens digit. I crossed out dates whose ones digit was smaller than 7. Then I subtracted to find the difference that was the same as the tens.

6. WRITE Math Explain the steps you used to determine the date of Rory's party in exercise 2.

[Order of steps may vary.] I crossed out all the one-digit dates. I crossed out all the even-numbered dates. I crossed out all remaining dates whose digits create a sum of more than 2 or less than 2.

Name________________ Lesson 2.1

Comparing Roman Numerals

In Roman numerals…

M = 1,000, so you can think of M as a base-ten thousands block.

C = 100, so you can think of C as a base-ten hundreds block.

X = 10, so you can think of X as a base-ten tens block.

V = 5, so you can think of V as half of a base-ten block or 5 base-ten ones blocks.

I = 1, so you can think of I as a base-ten ones block.

Compare the Roman numerals. Use the >, <, or = signs.

1. I (<) II
2. X (>) I
3. XII (>) XI
4. C (<) M
5. C (>) X
6. CC (>) CXX
7. M (>) CCC
8. CI (>) XII
9. V (>) I
10. V (<) X
11. XV (<) C
12. VIII (<) X

Think About It!

13. On a number line, which Roman numeral would fall farther to the left: C or X?

    X

14. On a number line, which Roman numeral would fall farther to the right: I or X?

    X

15. WRITE Math How many Cs are equal to one M?

    10 Cs

Name__________

You Give the Order

Use the 4 numbers at the bottom of the page to make twelve 4-digit numbers. Write the numbers on the lines in the first column. Order the numbers from least to greatest on the lines in the second column.

The 12 numbers will vary. They can be any of the following:

The 12 numbers will vary. Then check the order for accuracy.

3,479;	Least 7,349;
3,497;	7,394;
3,749;	7,439;
3,794;	7,493;
3,947;	7,934,
3,974;	7,943;
4,379;	9,347;
4,397;	9,374;
4,739;	9,437;
4,793;	9,473;
4,937;	9,734;
4,973;	Greatest 9,743.

Check for accuracy.

7 4 9 3

Think About It!

1. WRITE Math What is the greatest 4-digit number you can make with 7, 4, 9, and 3?
9,743

2. WRITE Math How did you find an answer to exercise 1? Explain.
Possible Answer: I placed the largest number in the largest place value and so on.

Name__________

Number Line Matchup

Match the data to the number line that shows it.

Number Line A
Number Line B
Number Line C
Number Line D

75 80 85 90 95 100 105 110 115 120 125 130 135 140 145 150 155 160 165 170 175

1. A stereo system costs $150, a CD collection costs $115, a speaker set costs $100, and a CD burner costs $120. Which number line shows this data?
C

2. Bill's dog weighs 90 pounds, Carl's dog weighs 75 pounds, Gail's dog weighs 100 pounds, and Stella's dog weighs 115 pounds. Which number line shows this data?
A

3. A jar of marbles contains 80 red marbles, 115 green marbles, 100 yellow marbles, and 75 blue marbles. Which number line shows this data?
D

4. There are 150 students in the 1st grade, 80 students in the 2nd grade, 100 students in the 3rd grade, and 120 students in the 4th grade. Which number line shows this data?
B

Think About It!

5. **Stretch Your Thinking** Rewrite exercise 4 to match the data shown on number line C.
Possible answer: There are 150 students in the 1st grade, 115 students in the 2nd grade, 100 students in the 3rd grade, and 120 students in the 4th grade.

6. WRITE Math How did you decide which number line matched each set of data?
Possible answer: I matched the data to the points plotted on each number line.

Name

Lesson 2.4

Fishing for Tens

Round the numbers in the fish below to the nearest ten. Then color the fish with crayons or colored pencils according to the table below.

10 and 60:	20 and 70:	30 and 80:	40 and 90:	50 and 100:
BLUE	RED	GREEN	YELLOW	PURPLE

64 **60** B
34 **30** G
99 **100** R
49 **50** P
82 **80** G
92 **90** Y
9 **10** B
12 **10** B
18 **20** R
69 **70** R
23 **20** R
43 **40** Y
37 **40** Y
29 **30** G
73 **70** R
96 **100** P
52 **50** P
61 **60** B
78 **80** G
87 **90** Y

Name

Lesson 2.5

Jellybean Rounding

A large jar is filled with jellybeans. The person whose guess comes closest to the actual number of jellybeans in the jar will win a prize.

1. Zoey guesses that there are 748 jellybeans in the jar. Rounded to the nearest hundred, she says her guess is about 750. Is Zoey's estimation reasonable? Explain.
   No. She rounded to the nearest ten.
2. Vic guesses that there are 852 jellybeans in the jar. Rounded to the nearest hundred, he says his guess is about 800. Is Vic's estimation resonable? Explain.
   No. 852 rounded to the nearest hundred is 900.
3. Wally guesses that there are 937 jellybeans in the jar. Rounded to the nearest hundred, he says his guess is about 900. Is Wally's estimation reasonable? Explain.
   Yes; 937 rounds to 900 when rounding to the nearest hundred.
4. Tracy guesses that there are 1,061 jellybeans in the jar. Rounded to the nearest hundred, she says her guess is about 1,000. Is Tracy's estimation reasonable? Explain.
   No. 1,061 rounded to the nearest hundred is 1,100.

Think About It!

5. **Stretch Your Thinking** The contest official says that there are actually 987 jellybeans in the jar. Rounded to the nearest hundred, how many jellybeans are in the jar?
   1,000
6. WRITE Math Whose guess, before rounding, came closest to 987? Explain.
   Possible answer: Wally; Wally's guess of 937 was 50 less than the actual 987, whereas Tracy's guess of 1,061 was off by 74, so Wally's guess was closest.

Name________________________

Rounding Riddles

Use the pictures below to solve the riddles.

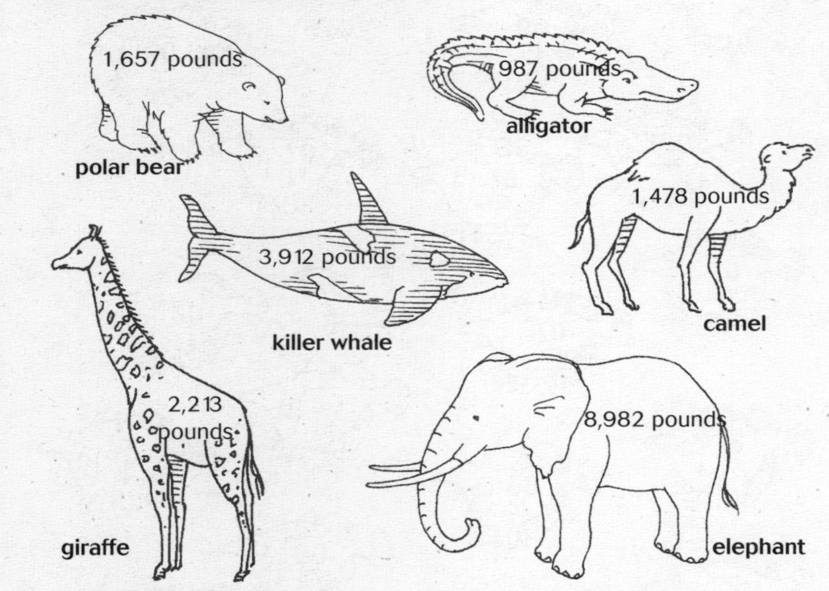

1. I live in the Arctic. I can smell a seal from 20 miles away. I weigh about 2,000 pounds. I am a/an **a polar bear**

2. I live in freshwater. I have a long tail and very sharp teeth. I weigh about 1,000 pounds. I am a/an **an alligator**

3. I live on the savannah. My neck is so long I can eat the tops of the trees! I weigh about 2,000 pounds. I am a/an **a giraffe**

4. I might have one bulge or two bulges on my back. I can go for days without drinking water. I weigh about 1,000 pounds. I am a/an **a camel**

5. I live in forests in Asia and Africa. I have big ears and a short tail. I weigh about 9,000 pounds. I am a/an **an elephant**

6. I swim in the ocean. I have fins, but I'm a mammal. I weigh about 4,000 pounds. I am a/an **a killer whale**

Name________________________

Property Paths

The map below shows a neighborhood park. The map also shows the number of steps it takes to go from one place to another within the park. Use this information to answer the following questions.

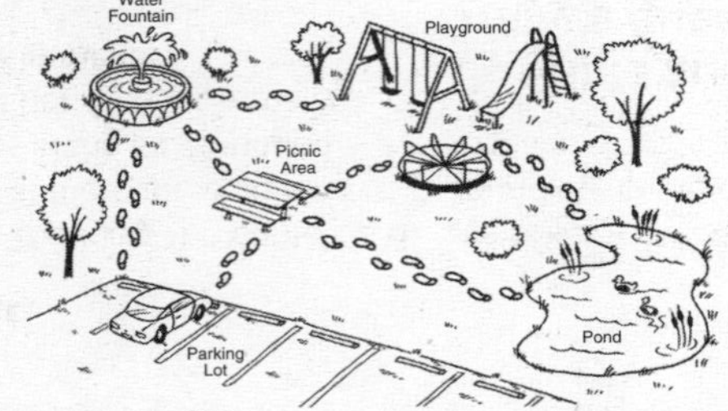

1. Megan starts at the parking lot, goes to the water fountain, and then goes to the picnic area. How many steps does Megan take in all? **10 steps**

2. Jim starts at the pond, goes to the picnic area, goes to the playground, and then goes to the water fountain. How many steps does Jim take in all? **16 steps**

3. Lily starts at the playground. She takes 16 steps in all, to reach the pond. Describe the path Lily takes. **Lily went from the playground to the water fountain, to the picnic area, to the pond.**

4. Rory starts at the parking lot. He takes 14 steps in all, to reach the picnic area. Describe the path Roy takes. **Rory went from the parking lot to the water fountain, to the playground, to the picnic area.**

Think About It!

5. **Stretch Your Thinking** Describe a path through the park that is 18 steps long. **Possible answer: I start at the pond, go to the picnic area, go to the playground, and then go back to the pond.**

6. WRITE Math Explain how you determined which path Rory followed in Exercise 4. **Possible answer: I tried different paths until I found a path that had a sum of 14 steps.**

Name________________ Lesson 3.2

Mystery Addends

Use the clues below to name the mystery added.

1. Add me to 5 for a sum of 12. What addend am I?
   $5 + \square = 12$
   The mystery addend is **7**.
2. Add 3 to me to total 11. What addend am I?
   $\square + 3 = 11$
   The mystery addend is **8**.
3. Double me to find a sum of 8. What addend am I?
   $\square + \square = 8$
   The mystery addend is **4**.
4. Add 9 to me to total 14. What addend am I?
   $\square + 9 = 14$
   The mystery addend is **5**.
5. Add me to 7 for a sum of 13. What addend am I?
   $7 + \square = 13$
   The mystery addend is **6**.
6. Add me to 8 to total 8. What addend am I?
   $8 + \square = 8$
   The mystery addend is **0**.
7. Add me to a number 2 more than me to find a sum of 8. What addend am I? What is the other addend?
   $\square + \square = 8$
   The mystery addends are **3, 5**.
8. Add me to a number 3 less than me to get a sum of 9. What addend am I? What is the other addend?
   $\square + \square = 9$
   The mystery addends are **6, 3**.

Think About It!

9. WRITE Math Why do you need to know the sum to find a missing addend?
   Possible answer: I use related subtraction facts to find a missing addend so I need to know the sum to know what number to subtract from.
10. **Stretch Your Thinking** The sum of two addends is 11. One of these addends plus itself results in a sum of 4. What are the two addends?
   2 and 9

Name________________ Lesson 3.3

Jellybean Estimation

Write whether the estimations are reasonable or not reasonable. If the estimations are not reasonable, write a reasonable estimation.

1. John was told that there were (121 + 342) jellybeans in a jar, so he estimated that there were 600 jellybeans in the jar. Is John's estimate reasonable?
   no; 400 or 460
2. Karl was told that there were (802 − 698) jellybeans in a jar, so he estimated that there were 100 jellybeans in the jar. Is Karl's estimate reasonable?
   yes
3. Suzy was told that there were (80 + 16) jellybeans in a jar, so she estimated that there were 150 jellybeans in the jar. Is Suzy's estimate reasonable?
   no; 95 or 100
4. Jade was told that there were (65 − 22) jellybeans in a jar, so she estimated that there were 50 jellybeans in the jar. Is Jade's estimate reasonable?
   yes
5. Ray was told that there were (181 + 45) jellybeans in a jar, so he estimated that there were 230 jellybeans in the jar. Is Ray's estimate reasonable?
   yes
6. Sara was told that there were 997 jellybeans in a jar so she estimated that there were 990 jellybeans in the jar. Is Sara's estimate reasonable?
   no; 1000

Think About It!

7. WRITE Math How did you know whether or not Sara's estimate is reasonable in exercise 6?
   Possible answer; I used rounding, Sara was definitely wrong whether rounding to the nearest thousand, hundred, or ten
8. **Stretch Your Thinking** If you were told that there were (435 + 237) jellybeans in a jar, what would your estimated sum be for this amount?
   Possible answers; 600, 670, 680

Name________________ Lesson 3.4

Find the Missing Number

Write in the missing number/s for each problem.

1. ■6 + 78 = 124 **4**
2. 27 + 5■ = 84 **7**
3. 1■ + 46 = 61 **5**
4. 56 + ■2 = 78 **2**
5. 32 + 1■ = 51 **9**
6. ■6 + 67 = 93 **2**
7. 41 + ■■ = 98 **57**
8. 6■ + ■8 = 100 **2; 3**
9. ■■ + 48 = 104 **56**
10. 22 + 79 + ■6 = 157 **5**
11. 56 + ■■ + 45 = 133 **32**
12. ■4 + 2■ + 18 = 80 **3; 8**

Think About It!

13. WRITE Math Explain how you found the missing numbers in Exercise 9.

Possible answer: I thought "what number + 8 = 14? (6)" and "what number + 1 + 4 = 10? (5)."

14. **Stretch Your Thinking** How would your answer for Exercise 6 change if the sum was 103 instead of 93?

The missing number would be 3 instead of 2.

Name________________ Lesson 3.5

Use Palindromes to Add

A *palindrome* is a word or phrase that reads the same forward and backward. Some numbers are palindromes too.

Read forward: 909

Read backward: 909

Start with any 3-digit number. 153
Reverse it. + 351
Add. 504
Reverse the sum. + 405
Add. 909
Continue reversing and adding until you reach a palindrome.

Use the method from above to find a palindrome for the following exercises. Show your work.

1. 143 **143 + 341 = 484**
2. 241 **241 + 142 = 383**
3. 431 **431 + 134 = 565**
4. 162 **162 + 261 = 423**
423 + 324 = 747

Think About It!

5. **Stretch Your Thinking** Write your own 3-digit number, then reverse and add to find its palindrome. Show your work below.

Possible answer: 402 + 204 = 606.

6. WRITE Math Explain whether the statement below is true or false. *When you add two numbers that are palindromes, the sum will always be a palindrome.*

The statement is false. Possible answer: If any digit has a value greater than or equal to 5, the sum will not be a palindrome.

Name____________ Lesson 3.6

Addition Squares

Fill in the empty boxes by adding the numbers across each row and down each column.

1.

854	274	**1,128**
604	874	**1,478**
1,458	**1,148**	**2,606**

2.

3,214	2,370	**5,584**
2,454	135	**2,589**
5,668	**2,505**	**8,173**

3.

2,695	1,002	**3,697**
611	1,134	**1,745**
3,306	**2,136**	**5,442**

4.

986	1,734	**2,720**
1,209	2,369	**3,578**
2,195	**4,103**	**6,298**

5.

3,420	2,030	**5,450**
2,462	1,559	**4,021**
5,882	**3,589**	**9,471**

6.

260	628	**888**
953	1,443	**2,396**
1,213	**2,071**	**3,284**

Think About It!

7. Draw your own addition square. Have the sum in the last box, of the third row, equal 4,098.

Answers will vary. Check students' addition squares.

8. **Stretch Your Thinking** In Exercise 6, what would happen to the sum in the last box, of the third row, if you flipped the positions of 260 and 1,443?

The sum will stay the same.

Name____________ Lesson 3.7

Addition Riddles

Use the letters in the boxes to solve each addition riddle below.

1. What can you catch but not throw?

A C O L D
8 10 2 6 12

10 D +2	1 O +1	3 L +3
1 C +9	5 A +3	

2. What goes up and down without moving?

S T A I R S
10 7 3 18 14 10

3 R +11	5 T +2	9 I +9
1 A +2	5 S +5	

Think About It!

3. **Stretch Your Thinking** Would the answer to exercise 1 still match the riddle without the A? Explain.

Possible Answer: No; you need the A before it or it will not make sense.

4. **Stretch Your Thinking** Could the answer to the riddle in exercise 2 still make sense without the second 10? Explain.

Possible Answer: No; One stair does not go up and down

Name__________

Lesson 4.1

Estimate Change

Charlie has a pair of cargo pants with six different pockets labeled 1-6. Each pocket contains a different money amount as shown in the key below.

Pocket
1 = $39
2 = $14
3 = $102
4 = $15
5 = $121
6 = $33

Estimate the differences of the money amounts in the pockets below.

1. Pocket 5 – Pocket 2 =

   ____ – ____ = ■

   Possible Answers: $105; $110; $90

2. Pocket 3 – Pocket 6 =

   ____ – ____ = ■

   Possible Answers: $70; $65

3. Pocket 1 – Pocket 2 =

   ____ – ____ = ■

   Possible Answers: $30; $25

4. Pocket 1 – Pocket 6 =

   ____ – ____ = ■

   Possible Answers: $10; $5

5. Pocket 4 – Pocket 2 =

   ____ – ____ = ■

   Possible Answers: $10; $5

6. Pocket 5 – Pocket 4 =

   ____ – ____ = ■

   Possible Answers: $105; $100; $80; $75

Think About It!

7. WRITE Math How did you estimate to find the answer to exercise 5? Is this answer close to the actual answer?

   Possible answer: I rounded to the nearest ten giving me $20 – 10 = $10. No the actual answer is $1.

8. **Stretch Your Thinking** How would your answer to exercise 6 change, if pocket 4 contained $121?

   The answer would then be 0 if you rounded each pocket the same way.

Name__________

Lesson 4.2

Find the Missing Digit

Oh no! Billy's homework was smudged when he took the paper out of his wet backpack. Write the missing digit/s for each problem.

1. (4)5 – 12 = 33
2. 27 – 1(5) = 12
3. 3(2) – 17 = 15
4. 83 – (3)7 = 46
5. 92 – 2(8) = 64
6. (7)6 – 47 = 29
7. 43 – 2(5) = 18
8. 7(2) – 29 = 43
9. (7)4 – 57 = 17
10. 5(3) – 18 = 35
11. 92 – (6)(6) = 26
12. (8)3 – 2(8) = 55

Think About It!

13. WRITE Math Explain how you found the missing digits for exercises 1 and 7.

    Possible answer: For #1, I added 12 + 33 = 45, so B = 4. For #7, I subtracted 43 – 18 = 25, so B = 5.

14. **Stretch Your Thinking** Explain how and why your answer to exercise 6 would change if the difference were 39 instead of 29.

    The missing number would be 8 instead of 7 because I'd have to add 10.

Name____________________ Lesson 4.3

Subtraction Models

Each exercise below uses base-ten blocks to model a 3-digit number. Choose a different 3-digit number to subtract from the given number. Use the base ten blocks to show how you would subtract the number you chose. Then record your subtraction in the column on the right.

Check students' models. Possible subtraction sentences for 1–4 given.

1.		226 − 119 = 107
2.		173 − 158 = 15
3.		238 − 154 = 84
4.		329 − 64 = 265

Think About It!

5. **Stretch Your Thinking** What if you chose a number equal to the one represented by the base-ten blocks for exercise 4? How would your answer change?

Possible answer: It would now be 0.

Name____________________ Lesson 4.4

Difference Number Puzzle

					A 5	6	1	8
					3		7	
				B 4	5	2		6
				3		C 4	9	0
	F 1			8			4	
	D 6	2	1	0			2	
	3							
E 7	8	3						

Find each difference. Then write your answer in the number cross above.

Across	Down
A 8,176 − 2,558	**F** 3,883 − 2,245
B 1,275 − 823	**G** 5,435 − 1,054
C 1,336 − 846	**H** 9,223 − 3,899
D 9,792 − 3,582	**I** 1,228 − 286
E 5,568 − 4,785	**J** 2,343 − 583

Think About It!

1. **Stretch Your Thinking** Write a different subtraction problem that could be used to result in the same answer for clue B.

   Possible answer: − 369

2. WRITE Math Explain how your answer for clue A helped you check your answers for clues C, H, and J.

   Possible answer: I could use the digits from the difference found from clue A to check my differences for clues C, H, and J.

Name________________

Subtraction Rectangles

Subtract across each row and down each column to fill in the empty boxes.

1.

808	308	500
368	52	316
440	256	184

2.

750	418	332
149	42	107
601	376	225

3.

9,208	4,318	4,890
3,818	1,277	2,541
5,390	3,041	2,349

4.

8,556	5,402	3,154
5,062	2,917	2,145
3,494	2,485	1,009

5.

8,349	2,899	5,450
3,277	1,664	1,613
5,072	1,235	3,837

6.

9,600	4,490	5,110
4,629	1,527	3,102
4,971	2,963	2,008

Think About It!

7. Fill out your own subtraction rectangle. Use 2,551 as shown.

		2,551

Check students' subtraction squares.

8. **Stretch Your Thinking** In exercise 6, how would the difference in the bottom right box be affected if 1,527 were changed to 1,327? Explain.

4,629 − 1,327 = 3,302; 5,110 − 3,302 = 1,808. So 2,008 becomes 1,808.

Name________________

Operation Choice

Caroline wrote the steps she used to solve her homework problems in order, and then gave the answer. Write a word problem that Caroline could have solved using her steps. Possible answers given for 1–4

1. Subtract 148 − 29,
   Add 53 to the difference.
   Answer: 172 stamps
   Sarah has 148 stamps. She gives 29 stamps to her younger brother. She then collects 53 more stamps. How many stamps does Sarah have now?

2. Add 18 + 45.
   Add the sum to 378.
   Answer: 441 stickers
   Marcus gives 18 stickers to his friends and 45 stickers to his sister. He has 378 stickers left. How many stickers did Marcus have to begin with?

3. Subtract 125 from 452.
   Subtract 58 from the difference.
   Answer: 269 paintings
   The museum contains 452 paintings. In one room there are 58 paintings. In another room there are 125 paintings. The rest of the paintings are in storage. How many paintings are in storage?

4. Add 158 + 243.
   Subtract 348 from the sum.
   Answer: 53 tickets
   On Friday, students sold 348 tickets to the play. On Saturday, 158 tickets were sold. On Sunday, 243 tickets were sold. How many more tickets were sold on Saturday and Sunday combined, than were sold on Friday?

Think About It!

5. WRITE Math Explain how you decided what problem to write for exercise 1.
   Answers may vary. Check students' explanations for reasonableness.

6. **Stretch Your Thinking** Write a multi-step problem, like the ones above. Then show the operations you would use to solve this problem.
   Answers may vary. Check students' problems and operations.

Name________________ Lesson 4.7

Two-Part Patterns

Some patterns may have two parts that make up the pattern rule.

10	12	16	18	22	24	28	30
+2	+4	+2	+4	+2	+4	+2	

Fill in the missing numbers in the boxes for the given patterns below.

1. 10 + 4 **14** − 2 **12** + 4 16 − 2 **14** + 4 18 + 4 **16**
2. **19** + 6 25 − 1 24 + 6 30 − 1 **29** + 6 35 − 1 **34**
3. 12 − 3 9 + 10 **19** − 3 **16** + 10 **26** − 3 23 + 10 **33**
4. 17 − 1 **16** + 1 17 − 1 **16** + 1 17 − 1 **16** + 1 17

Think About It!

5. Stretch Your Thinking What is the pattern for these seven numbers?

2 9 3 10 4 11 5

add 7, subtract 6

Name________________ Lesson 4.8

Estimate or Exact Time?

Several children go to the Discovery Center on a rainy afternoon. For each situation, complete the statement using words or numbers.

USE DATA For 1-5 use the table below.

Discovery Center Activities	
Activity	**Time**
Rock Wall	75 minutes
Ball Bounce	10 minutes
Laser Tag	35 minutes
Explore Space	60 minutes
Tumble Mats	20 minutes

1. Miranda wants to play laser tag and go to the explore space activity.

   Miranda will need about **100** minutes for her activities.

2. Jin spends about half an hour at the Discovery Center.

   List each possible activitie Jin could take part in at the Discovery Center during this time.

   ball bounce, laser tag, tumble mats

3. Terry is going to the Discovery Center for 45 minutes. He wants to take part in two activities. Which activities could Terry take part in to fill this time?

   laser tag and ball bounce

4. Carmen wants to climb the rock wall at the Discovery Center.

   Carmen will need about **180** minutes for this activity.

5. Marty is going to the Discovery Center for 60 minutes. Which activity can Marty not choose to do?

   rock wall

Think About It!

6. WRITE Math Explain how you found the answer for exercise 1.

   Possible answer: I estimated the time needed for the two activities (about 100 minutes).

7. **Stretch Your Thinking** Show all the possible combinations of activities Aidan could do in 60 minutes.

   explore space; laser tag and tumble mats; laser tag and ball bounce; tumble mats and ball bounce

Name____________________________ Lesson 5.1

Related Apples

Fill in the missing art to make each related addition and multiplication sentence true.

1. + + =

× ________ =

2. ________ + ________ =

× = ________

Think About It!

3. WRITE Math How did you know how many apples to multiply to arrive at the product shown in exercise 1?

   Possible Answer: I knew that only 3 X 3 = 9

4. WRITE Math How did you know how many apples to add to arrive at the sum shown in exercise 2?

   Possible Answer: I added 4 since 4 was being multiplied in the related multiplication sentence.

Name____________________________ Lesson 5.2

Quilt Arrays

You want to make a quilt using arrays of 5 different colors. Each color represents a different product. Make a list of the colors and arrays you use. Then color your quilt. The quilt has been started in black.

$2 \times 2 = 4$ gray squares

____ x ____ = ____ ________ squares

____ x ____ = ____ ________ squares

____ x ____ = ____ ________ squares

____ x ____ = ____ ________ squares

____ x ____ = ____ ________ squares

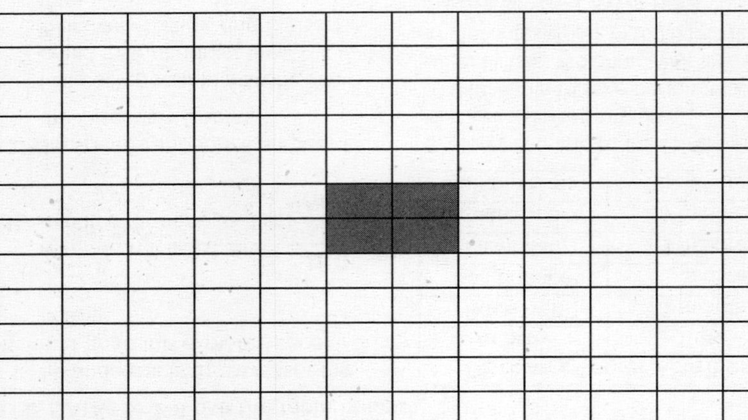

Designs will vary. Check to see that students have made accurate multiplication equations for the arrays they colored.

Name______________________________ Lesson 5.3

Pairs Dilemma!

Match up the problem in Column A with the number sentence that solves it in Column B.

Column A	Column B
1. Edgar washed 24 pairs of socks. How many socks did Edgar wash in all?	$34 = 2 \times 17$
2. Keith sees 23 pairs of mittens in a store. How many mittens does Keith see in all?	$18 \times 2 = 36$
3. In a closet are 3 pairs of white sneakers, 2 pairs of brown shoes, and 4 pairs of black shoes. How many shoes are in the closet in all?	$3 \times 2 = 6$ $2 \times 2 = 4$ $\quad 6 + 4 + 8 = 18$ $4 \times 2 = 8$
4. Each of Farmer Lee's chickens lays 2 eggs each week. She has 14 chickens. How many eggs do Farmer Lee's chickens lay each week?	$24 \times 2 = 48$
5. Caroline made 18 vests. She wants to put 2 pockets on each vest. How many pockets should Caroline cut out?	$32 = 2 \times 16$
6. Santiago builds bikes. He has 32 bicycle wheels. If each bicycle takes 2 wheels, then what is the maximum number of bicycles Santiago can build?	$23 \times 2 = 46$
7. Tina made 34 earrings. How many pairs of earrings did Tina make?	$2 \times 14 = 28$

Think About It!

8. **Stretch Your Thinking** Mila is sorting 13 pairs of colored socks. If 10 of the socks are black, and 8 are blue, how many socks are not blue or black?

8 socks.

9. WRITE Math How did you find the answer to exercise 3?

Possible Answer: I know there would be 3 producth added together to find the final sum.

Name______________________________ Lesson 5.4

Detective Four Paws

Fill in the missing information in each problem.

1. Mrs. Park's dog tracked footprints all over the house. Mrs. Park multiplied **8** × 4 to find that she needed to clean up 32 prints.

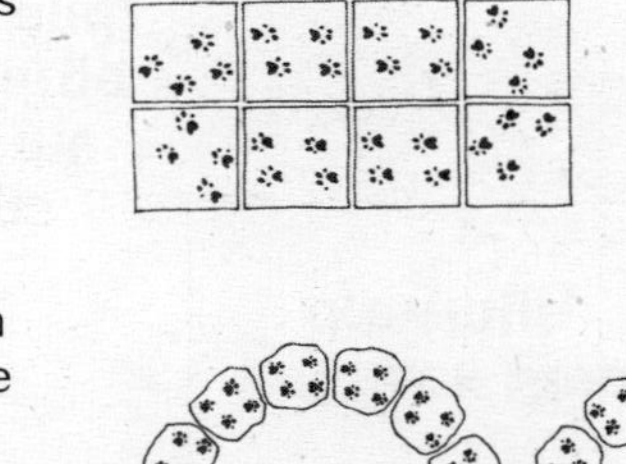

2. Mrs. Washington's cat stepped in paint. Then the cat walked on the stone path. Mrs. Washington multiplied 4 × 1, and found that there were **44** prints that she needed to wash off.

3. Cole saw these deer tracks in the snow. He multiplied **4** × 10 to find that there were 40 deer tracks in the snow.

4. Mrs. Tinis **12** horses all need new horse shoes. Each horse has 4 hoores heeding a horse shoe on each hoof. Tina found that she needed 48 horse shoes.

5. Ms. Butcher's 15 sled dogs wear booties on their feet when they race. How many booties does Ms. Butcher need in all to shoe the feet of all of her sled dogs?

60 booties

Name________________ **Lesson 5.5**

How Many Seeds in a Row?

Farmer Holmes wants to plant corn in rows. He wants to leave every other row empty. This will leave space for him to walk between rows.

Fill in the blanks below to show what Farmer Holmes plants. The first two rows have been done for you.

Row	
Row 1	$10 \times 1 = 10$ seeds
Row 2	$10 \times 0 = 0$ seeds
Row 3	**9** x 1 = 9 seeds
Row 4	9 x **0** = **0** seeds
Row 5	**8** x 1 = 8 seeds
Row 6	8 x **0** = **0** seeds
Row 7	**7** x **1** = 7 seeds
Row 8	7 x **0** = **0** seeds
Row 9	**6** x **1** = 6 seeds
Row 10	6 x **0** = **0** seeds

Now fill in the rows with the correct number of seed pictures.

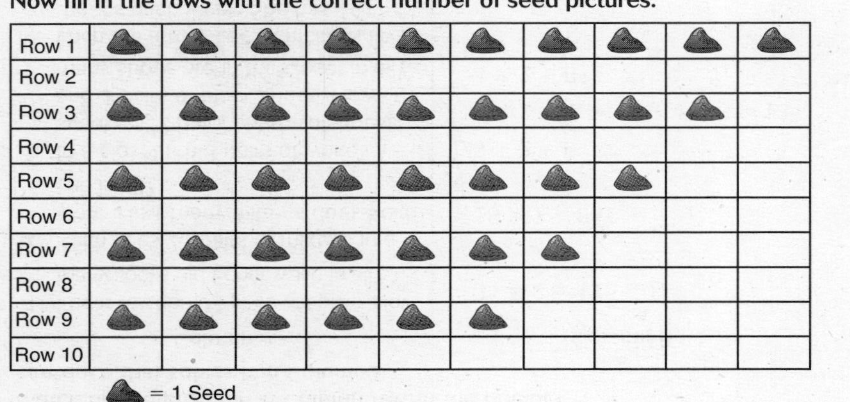

Name________________ **Lesson 5.6**

4 Tables

Draw a picture to solve each problem. Each drawing should show an arrangement of the 4 tables below. Each table can fit up to 4 chairs.

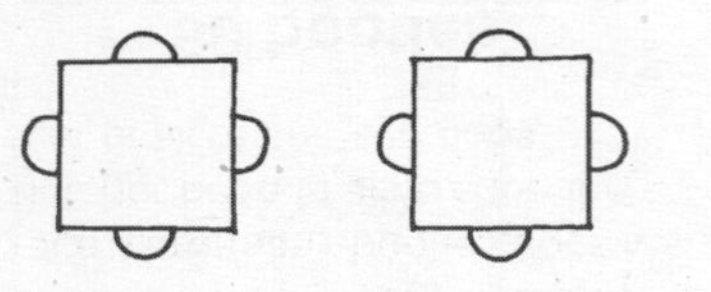

1. There are 4 tables in a lunch room. If 4 people sit at each lunch table, how many people sit in the lunch room in all?
   16 people

   Check Studetns drawings

2. Ten people want to sit at the 4 tables. What is the best way to arrange the tables so that the maximum number of people can talk to one another?
   Check students' drawings. Possible solution: If the 4 tables in a row are pushed together, there is room for

   Check Studetns drawings

3. Eight people want to sit at the 4 tables. What is the best way to arrange the 4 tables so that everyone can talk to one another?
   Check students' drawings. Possible solution: Push the 4 tables together make 1 large square (two tables wide and 2 tables deep). Then 8 people can sit at the table.

   Check Studetns drawings

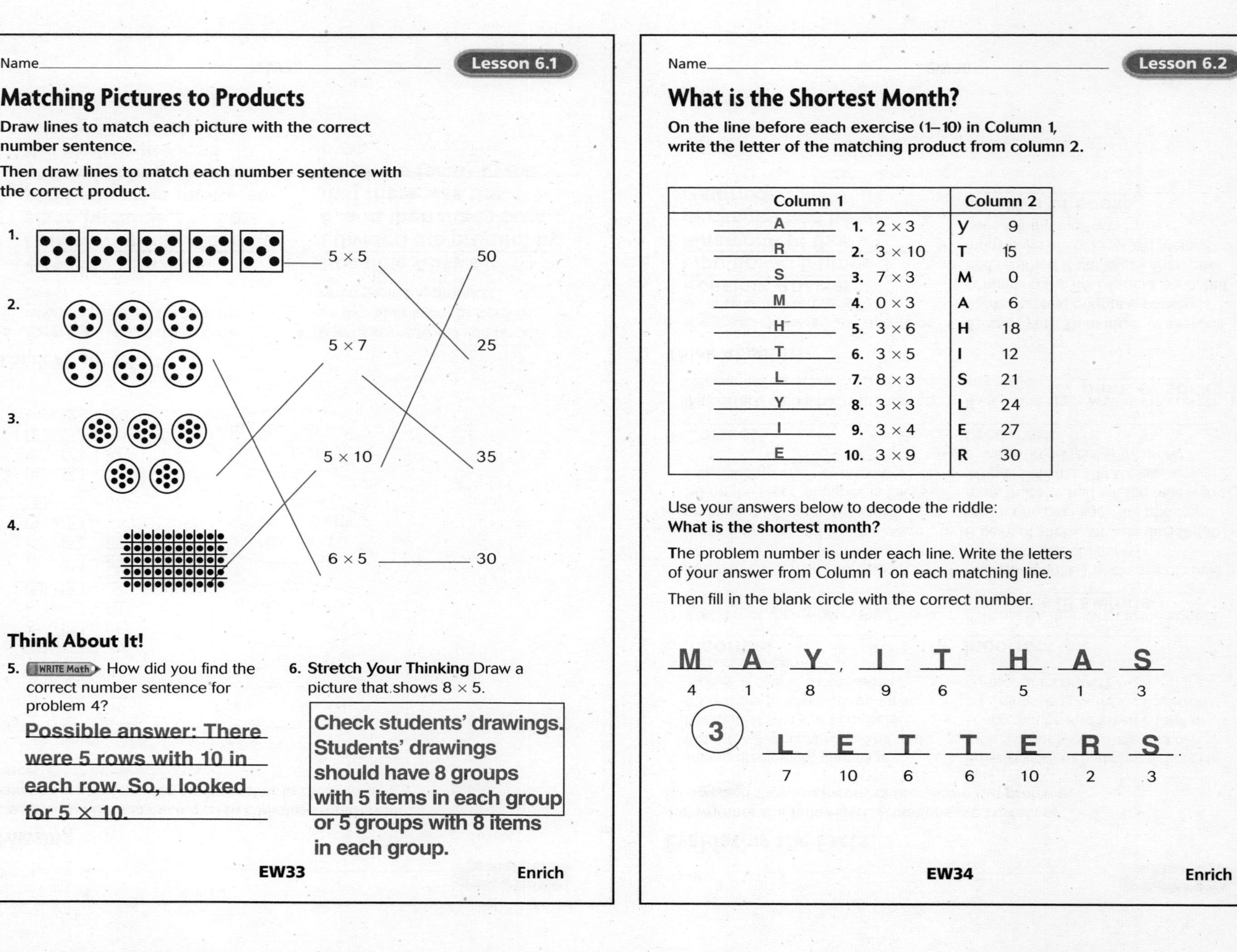

Name

Matching Pictures to Products

Draw lines to match each picture with the correct number sentence.

Then draw lines to match each number sentence with the correct product.

1. 5×5 — 50
2. 5×7 — 25
3. 5×10 — 35
4. 6×5 — 30

Think About It!

5. WRITE Math How did you find the correct number sentence for problem 4?

Possible answer: There were 5 rows with 10 in each row. So, I looked for 5×10.

6. **Stretch Your Thinking** Draw a picture that shows 8×5.

Check students' drawings. Students' drawings should have 8 groups with 5 items in each group or 5 groups with 8 items in each group.

Name

What is the Shortest Month?

On the line before each exercise (1–10) in Column 1, write the letter of the matching product from column 2.

Column 1		Column 2	
A	1. 2×3	y	9
R	2. 3×10	T	15
S	3. 7×3	M	0
M	4. 0×3	A	6
H	5. 3×6	H	18
T	6. 3×5	I	12
L	7. 8×3	S	21
Y	8. 3×3	L	24
I	9. 3×4	E	27
E	10. 3×9	R	30

Use your answers below to decode the riddle:
What is the shortest month?

The problem number is under each line. Write the letters of your answer from Column 1 on each matching line.

Then fill in the blank circle with the correct number.

M A Y, I T H A S
4 1 8 9 6 5 1 3

(3) L E T T E R S.
7 10 6 6 10 2 3

Name________________ Lesson 6.3

Missing

Use the numbers in each oval to complete 4 different number sentences. Use each number in the oval only once.

1. 6 × [8] = [48]
   [6] × [6] = 36
   6 × [1] = [6]
   [6] × [7] = 42

   (6) (8) (48) (7)
   (6) (6) (6) (1)

2. [6] × [7] = 42
   6 × [11] = [66]
   6 × [9] = [54]
   [6] × [4] = 24

   (6) (66) (4) (7)
   (6) (9) (54) (11)

3. 6 × [12] = [72]
   6 × [5] = [30]
   [6] × [9] = 54
   [6] × [3] = 18

   (6) (12) (5) (3)
   (6) (9) (72) (30)

4. [6] × [2] = 12
   6 × [7] = [42]
   [6] × [10] = 60
   6 × [6] = [36]

   (6) (2) (42) (7)
   (6) (6) (36) (10)

Think About It!

5. WRITE Math How did you know where to place the 6's from the ovals?

   Possible Answer:
   I knew where to place the sixes because all of the products were multiples of 6, so I simply placed the 6's in equations missing both factors.

6. WRITE Math How did you decide on the other factor besides 6 when given the product.

   Possible Answer:
   I divided the product by 6, and then made sure that there was the resulting factor in the oval.

Name________________ Lesson 6.4

Evaluating the Facts

Tell whether the following calculations are correct or incorrect. If they are incorrect then solve the problem.

1. Joanie drank eight glasses of water for 7 straight days. She told her mother that she had drunk 63 glasses of water during those 7 days. Is Joanie's calculation correct or incorrect?

   Incorrect

   If incorrect, then what is the correct calculation? **56**

2. Edward went to batting practice. He took 9 swings, twice. He told his coach that he had taken a total of 21 swings. Is Edward's calculation correct or incorrect?

   Incorrect

   If incorrect, then what is the correct calculation? **18 swings**

3. Paul bowled 9 pins in 6 straight frames. He added up his score for those 6 frames and wrote it down on a piece of paper. He wrote 54 on the piece of paper. Is Paul's calculation correct or incorrect?

   Correct

   If incorrect, then what is the correct calculation? ________

4. Melissa bought 4 packages of socks. Each package contained 9 pairs of socks. Melissa decided to return one package. She told her mom that she had left the mall with 28 pairs of socks. Is Melissa's calculation correct or incorrect?

   Incorrect

   If incorrect, then what is the correct calculation? **27 pairs of socks**

Think About It!

5. WRITE Math How did you decide on an answer to exercise 4?

   Possible Answer:
   I multiplied 9 times 3 since one of the packages had been returned.

6. **Stretch Your Thinking** If, in exercise 4, Melissa had bought 6 packages containing 9 pairs of socks each, but had returned 2 packages, then how many pairs of socks would Melissa have left the mall with?

   36 pairs of socks

Name______________________ Lesson 6.5

How Many in One Week?

Each problem is missing key information. Find the missing information by using the information in the column *One Week* and acting out the solution.

	Problem	One Week
1.	John drinks milk everyday. He drinks 1 glass of milk for breakfast and __2__ glass(es) of milk for dinner.	John drinks 21 glasses of milk in *one week.*
2.	Ted reads in a book each day. He reads 2 pages in the morning and __2__ page(s) at night.	Ted reads 28 pages in *one week.*
3.	Ray's bus makes 3 stops on the way to school and __2__ stop(s) on the way home.	Ray's bus makes 35 stops in *one week.*
4.	Belinda writes 2 e-mails each day, to each of her friends. Belinda has __3__ friend(s).	Belinda writes 42 e-mails in *one week.*

Think About It!

5. WRITE Math How did you use the method "Act it Out" to help find the answer to exercise 2?

   Possible Answer: I flipped the pages in a book 28 times, then sectioned these flips into 7 days worth of groups which equaled 4.

6. **Stretch Your Thinking** If Belinda had written 84 e-mails in one week, then how many friends must she have?

   6 friends

Name______________________ Lesson 7.1

The Products of 8 Big Dipper

The Big Dipper is part of the constellation Ursa Major or the Great Bear. Find each product. Then use the products to help you draw the Big Dipper.

1. $8 \times 5 = $ **40**
2. $3 \times 8 = $ **24**
3. $8 \times 9 = $ **72**
4. $8 \times 2 = $ **16**
5. $4 \times 8 = $ **32**
6. $8 \times 1 = $ **8**
7. $6 \times 8 = $ **48**
8. $8 \times 8 = $ **64**
9. $8 \times 7 = $ **56**
10. $0 \times 8 = $ **0**

Below are numbers in the same positions as some of the stars of Ursa Major. You will connect the numbers that form the Big Dipper.

Begin at the number 32 (8 × 4). Connect this product to the next product of 8 (8 × 5) and s on until you reach 80.

32 40 48 56 80 64 16 0 72 8 24

32 to 40 to 48 to 56 to 64 to 72 to 80

Think About It!

11. **Stretch Your Thinking** Which two products of 8 would you connect to make the top of the dipper? Explain.

    Possible answer: Connecting 56 and 80 forms the top of the dipper or cup.

Name ____________ Lesson 7.2

9s Riddle

Find the product in Column 2 for each problem in Column 1. Then write the letter of the product on the line in front of the problem that it matches.

	Column 1	Column 2
W	1. 9×5	H 9
T	2. 0×9	M 36
N	3. 6×9	W 45
M	4. 4×9	R 63
H	5. 9×1	N 54
R	6. 9×7	O 18
Y	7. 8×9	A 27
A	8. 3×9	E 81
O	9. 2×9	Y 72
E	10. 9×9	D 99
B	11. 9×10	T 0
D	12. 11×9	B 90

Write the letter, that matches the following exercise numbers from Column 1, in the correct blank to make a riddle. Then answer the riddle.

H	O	W	M	A	N	Y	9s
5	9	1	4	8	3	7	

A	R	E	B	E	T	W	E	E	N
8	6	10	11	10	2	1	10	10	3

1	A	N	D	100?
	8	3	12	

Answer: 11 (99 counts for two 9s)

Name ____________ Lesson 7.3

Searching for Missing Factors

Find each missing factor. Then write the word form for the missing factor.

1. [9] $\times 7 = 63$ NINE
2. [1] $\times 7 = 7$ ONE
3. $7 \times$ [3] $= 21$ THREE
4. [5] $\times 7 = 35$ FIVE
5. [10] $\times 7 = 70$ TEN
6. [8] $\times 7 = 56$ EIGHT
7. [6] $\times 7 = 42$ SIX
8. [4] $\times 7 = 28$ FOUR
9. [2] $\times 7 = 14$ TWO
10. [7] $\times 7 = 49$ SEVEN

Find each word form for exercises 1–10 above in the word search below. Words are written horizontally, vertically, and diagonally, as well as forward and backward.

F	I	V	E	T	O	X	E
O	W	N	H	M	W	I	I
Q	E	R	I	R	T	S	G
F	E	I	R	N	E	V	H
E	O	U	V	F	E	N	T
J	O	Y	R	Z	G	M	O
F	I	N	E	V	E	S	N
F	T	E	N	J	Z	I	T

Name________________ **Lesson 7.4**

An Irregular Multiplication Table

Complete the *inverted* multiplication table below.
Be careful, this is not a regular multiplication table!

	10	9	8	7	6	5	4	3	2	1
10	100	90	80	70	60	50	40	30	20	10
9	90	81	72	63	54	45	36	27	18	9
8	80	72	64	56	48	40	32	24	16	8
7	70	63	56	49	42	35	28	21	14	7
6	60	54	48	42	36	30	24	18	12	6
5	50	45	40	35	30	25	20	15	10	5
4	40	36	32	28	24	20	16	12	8	4
3	30	27	24	21	18	15	12	9	6	3
2	20	18	16	14	12	10	8	6	4	2
1	10	9	8	7	6	5	4	3	2	1

Think About It!

1. WRITE Math How is this inverted table different from a regular multiplication table? Explain. **Possible answer: A regular multiplication table begins with 1 (or 0) in the upper left corner and the factors (and products) increase as you go down and to the right. In this table the factors (and products) increase as you move up and to the left.**

2. WRITE Math How can a multiplication table show the Commutative Property of Multiplication? Explain. **Possible answer: The table shows that each product can be arrived at in two ways. So 4 x 3 can be found from row 4 and column 3 or from row 3 and column 4, which corresponds to 3 x 4. Both 4 x 3 and 3 x 4 equal 12, demonstrating the Commutative Property of Multiplication.**

3. **Stretch Your Thinking** Which products appear only one time in the table? Describe the relationship these products share and the pattern they make. **Possible answer: 100, 81, 64, 49, 25, 1; these are all perfect square numbers—they have the same factor times itself—and form a diagonal through the middle of the table (from 100 to 1).**

Name________________ **Lesson 7.5**

Filling In

For exercises 1 and 3 write a word problem based on the information given in the table. For exercises 2 and 4 fill out the table based upon the information in the word problem.

1. **Answers will vary.**

Total Number of Flowers					
Bunches	1	2	3	4	5
Number of Flowers	8	16	24	32	40

2. A packaging company accidentally packed an equally increasing number of cookies into 5 straight boxes. The first box contained 6 cookies while the fifth box contained (6 cookies × 5 cookies). Fill out the table at the right showing an equal increase in the number of cookies per box.

Number of Cookies					
Boxes	1	2	3	4	5
Cookies per Box	6	**12**	**18**	**24**	**30**

3. **Answers will vary.**

Commulative Miles Hiked					
Day	1	2	3	4	5
Miles Hiked	5	10	15	20	25

4. Morgan placed all of his baseball cards into packages. He placed 4 cards into package number 1 and continued to add 4 cards to each additional package. Fill out the table at the right to show how many cards Morgan placed in each package.

Number of Cards Packaged					
Packages	1	2	3	4	5
Number of Cards per Package	4	**8**	12	**16**	**20**

Name________________ Lesson 8.1

Working Rules

Taylor did his homework last night, but needs someone to check it for him. Decide whether Taylor's answers are correct or incorrect. Then explain why.

1. Identify the Pattern and the Rule.

Bouquets of Flowers	2	3	4	5
Cost	$16	$24	$32	$40

Pattern: The cost of a bouquet equals the number of bouquets times 9.

Rule: Multiply the number of bouquets by 9.

Correct or incorrect?

incorrect

Explanation?

the rule is × 8;

2 × $8 = $16

2. Identify the Pattern and the Rule.

Tins of Popcorn	3	4	5	6
Cost	$15	$20	$25	$30

Pattern: The cost of a tin of popcorn equals the number of tins times 5.

Rule: Multiply the number of tins of popcorn by 5.

Correct or incorrect?

correct

Explanation?

the rule is multiply by 5

because 3 × $5 = $15

Think About It!

3. WRITE Math How did you find the answer for exercise 1?.

Possible Answer: I tested the student written rule and found it to be incorrect.

4. **Stretch Your Thinking** Rewrite the Student written rule, for the table below, to make it correct.

Package of Cookies	2	3	4	5
Cost	$6	$9	$12	$15

Multiply the number of bouquets by 9.

Name________________ Lesson 8.2

Factor Riddles?

Solve each riddle for the missing factor.

1. I am a product with the following factors: 1, 7, and 14. I am missing one factor. What factor am I missing?

2

2. I am a product with the following factors: 1, 3, 4, 6, and 12. I am missing one factor. What factor am I missing?

2

3. I am a product with factors such as 1 and 9. I am missing one factor. What factor am I missing?

3

4. My factors can be written using repeated addition as 5 + 5 + 5 + 5 + 5 + 5 + 5 + 5. What are my factors?

8 and 5

5. I am the same number as my product. I am equal to 5 + 2. What factor am I?

7

6. One of my factors is equal to 5 − 2. I am a product of 27. What factor am I missing?

9

7. I am a 2 digit product. One of my digits is the same as one of my factors, 8. The other digit is half of this factor. What product am I?

48

8. I am a product with the following factors: 1, 3, and 21. I am missing one factor. What factor am I missing?

7

Think About It!

9. WRITE Math Explain how you solved problem 7.

Possible answer: The product has the number 8 and half of this, or 4. The two possibilities are 48 and 84. Because 48 is divisible by 8, it must be the correct product.

10. WRITE Math Write your own factor riddle and solve it.

Answers will vary. Sample answer: My product is 30. One of my factors is equal to 3 × 2. What is one of my missing factors? 5

Name________________ Lesson 8.3

Matching Factors and Products

Read the number sentence in Column A. Then circle the correct product in Column B. In Column C, write a number sentence that results in the other products in Column B (the one that is not circled).

Possible answers for column C

Column A	Column B	Column C
1. $(9 \times 1) \times 7 =$ ☐	(63) 70	**(10 x 1) x 7 =**
2. $7 \times (4 \times 3) =$ ☐	(84) 49	**(7 x 1) x 7 =**
3. $8 \times (4 \times 2) =$ ☐	48 (64)	**8 x (2 x 3) =**
4. $(5 \times 2) \times 7 =$ ☐	(70) 49	**7 x (1 x 7) =**
5. $11 \times (3 \times 2) =$ ☐	(66) 55	**(11 x 1) x 5 =**
6. $3 \times (8 \times 2) =$ ☐	30 (48)	**(3 x 5) x 2 =**
7. $(6 \times 2) \times 6 =$ ☐	(72) 48	**(2 x 4) x 6 =**
8. $(3 \times 3) \times 9 =$ ☐	54 (81)	**(2 x 3) x 9 =**
9. $9 \times (3 \times 4) =$ ☐	(108) 63	**7 x (3 x 3) =**
10. $(7 \times 2) \times 4 =$ ☐	36 (56)	**6 x (3 x 2) =**
11. $(4 \times 6) \times 2 =$ ☐	(48) 20	**(5 x 2) x 2 =**

Name________________ Lesson 8.4

Mix-and-Match Properties

Gary tried to work out the following problems. He wrote the equation he used to solve, the property he used to solve, and his answer. Circle each part of Gary's work that is incorrect. Then rewrite the circled portions, making them correct.

1. The circus was open 5 days this week. I t was closed 2 days this week. If 12 people visited the circus each day it was open, then how many people visited the circus this week.

   (Equation: $0 \times 2 =$)

   Property: Commutative

   Answer: 60 people

   Rewrite: **12 × 5 =**

2. Paul gave a total of eight carrots to his rabbits. Each rabbit recieved the same number of carrots. Paul has eight rabbits. How many carrots did each of Paul's rabbits receive?

   Equation: $1 \times 8 =$

   (Property: Zero)

   Answer: 1 carrot

   Rewrite: **Identity**

3. Bobby collected 2 pieces of paper from each student in a ten-student class. Then he collected the same number of pieces of paper from 3 other classes. How many pieces of paper did Bobby collect in all?

   Equation: $(10 \times 2) \times 4 =$

   Property: Associative

   (Answer: 40 pieces of paper)

   Rewrite: **80 pieces of paper**

4. Gina dribbled the basketball for eleven seconds. She averaged 1 dribble per second. How many times did Gina dribble the basketball?

   Equation: $11 \times 1 =$

   Property: Identity

   Answer: 11 times

   Rewrite: **no rewrite**

Think About It!

1. WRITE Math How did you find the answer to exercise 2?.

   Possible Answer: I multiplied by 1 which is the Idenity property

Name________________

Multistep Countdown

Amy can't wait until her party. She counts down the number of days to this event. Match each number of days below with the multistep number sentence that represents it. Place the answer choices A–G on the answer lines correctly.

1. 48 days A	A $6 \times (3 \times 2) + 12$
2. 12 days G	B $(11 - 1) \div 10$
3. 26 days D	C $(10 \times 3) + 6$
4. 17 days E	D $(48 \div 2) + 2$
5. 36 days C	E $4 + 16 - 3$
6. 10 days F	F $2 + 2 + 2 + 2 + 2 + 2 - 2$
7. 1 day B	G $(6 \times 2) \div 1$

Think About It!

8. WRITE Math Does answer choice F represent the greatest number of days since it is the longest number sentence? Explain.

No; length of the number sentence has nothing to do with greatest value

9. **Stretch Your Thinking** What if exercise 7 had read 0 days? How might you write a multistep number sentence for this number?

Possible Answer; $(0 \times 8) \div 1$

Name________________

Matching Models

Draw a line to match each word problem with the correct model used to solve it. Write the division sentence used to solve the problem under each model.

1. Harriet has 18 sticks of gum. Each pack of gum contains 6 sticks. How many packs of gum does Harriet have?
2. Sean has 15 baseball cards. He groups them into 3s. How many groups of baseball cards does Sean have?
3. Lucy has a box of 24 cookies. She divides them equally among her 6 friends. How many cookies does each friend receive?
4. Eddie has 56 coins in his collection. He separates the coins into groups of 8. How many coins are in each of Eddie's groups?
5. Michael bought 54 juice boxes for a picnic. There will be 9 people at each picnic table. How many tables does Michael have juice boxes for, if each person will receive one juice box?
6. Leona ran for 27 minutes. She ran 3 miles. How long did it take Leona to run each mile?
7. Andy has 35 stickers. He wants to put 7 stickers on each page of his sticker book. How many pages will Andy need?

$24 \div 6 = 4$

$54 \div 9 = 6$

$18 \div 6 = 3$

$27 \div 3 = 9$

$15 \div 3 = 5$

$35 \div 7 = 5$

$56 \div 8 = 7$

Name________________ Lesson 9.2

Division and Subtraction Tank Exchange

A fish store just brought in some more fish tanks. They brought in enough tanks to divide the fish in their older tanks into equal groups. They can only take one group out at a time.

For each of the following division sentences there is also a picture of a fish tank filled with fish. Circle groups of fish representing each time you use repeated subtraction with a different color. Then write the answer to the division sentence.

1. 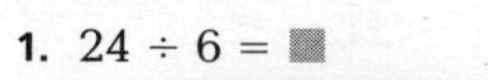

$24 \div 6 = ■$

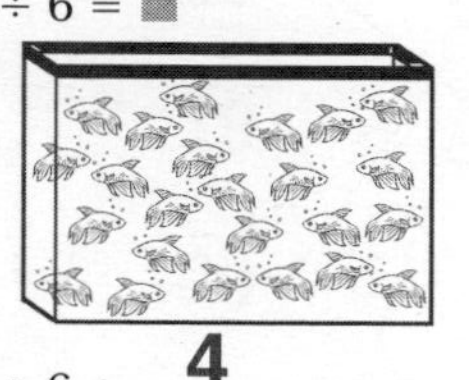

$24 \div 6 =$ **4**

Check student drawings, students should use 4 different colors to circle 4 groups of 6 fish

2. 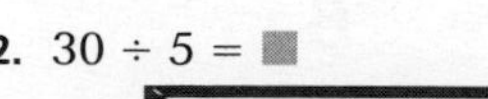

$30 \div 5 = ■$

$30 \div 5 =$ **6**

Check student drawings, students should use 6 different colors to circle 6 groups of 5 fish

3. 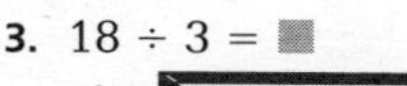

$18 \div 3 = ■$

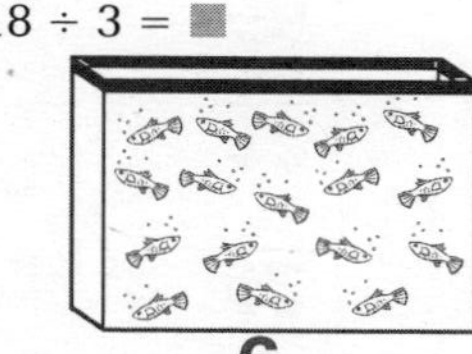

$18 \div 3 =$ **6**

check student drawings, students should use 6 different colors to circle 6 groups of 3 fish

4. $20 \div 4 = ■$

$20 \div 4 =$ **5**

check student drawings, students should use 5 different colors to circle 5 groups of 4 fish

Think About It!

5. WRITE Math How many different colors did you use to circle fish in exercise 3? Explain.

6; because the directions told me to use a different color for each group of fish I circled and $18 \div 3 = 6$

6. **Stretch Your Thinking** If exercise 4 was changed to $20 \div 5 = ■$ how would this affect the number of colors you would use to circle fish?

from 5 colors to 4; the number of colors would reduce by 1

Name________________ Lesson 9.3

Mystery Arrays

Use the clues to help solve the mystery arrays. You can use tiles or draw the array on a separate sheet of paper.

1. I am an array made with 24 tiles. I have 8 tiles in each row. How many rows do I have?
3 rows

2. I am an array with 4 rows. I have 16 tiles in all. How many columns do I have?
4 columns

3. I am an array with 7 tiles in each row. My number of rows is 4 less than the number of tiles in each of my rows. How many tiles do I have in all?
21 tiles

4. I am an array with 24 tiles. My number of rows is 5 more than the number of tiles in each of my rows. How many rows do I have?
8 rows

5. I am a square-shaped array. I have 7 rows. How many tiles do I have in all?
49 tiles

6. I am an array with 40 tiles. I have an odd number of rows and an even number of tiles in each row. The number of my rows plus the number of tiles in each of my rows is 13. How many rows do I have?
5 rows

Think About It!

7. Sarah has 37 tiles. She makes an array with 7 tiles in each row. How many rows does Sarah make?
5 rows

How many tiles are left over?
2 tiles

8. Sarah obtains 40 more tiles. She adds the 40 tiles to the tiles left over from her first array. She makes a new array with 7 tiles in each row. How many rows does Sarah make? Write the number sentence that shows this problem.
6 rows; $(40 + 2) \div 7 = 6$

9. WRITE Math Write your own mystery array. Include the answer.
Arrays will vary; check students' work.

Name____________________ Lesson 9.4

Multiplication and Division Match

Solve. Then draw a line to match each multiplication sentence to a comparable division sentence.

	Multiplication		Division
1.	$9 \times 7 =$ **63**	A	$12 \div 2 =$ **6**
2.	$5 \times 8 =$ **40**	B	$42 \div 7 =$ **6**
3.	$3 \times 9 =$ **27**	C	$18 \div 3 =$ **6**
4.	$6 \times 7 =$ **42**	D	$40 \div 8 =$ **5**
5.	$2 \times 6 =$ **12**	E	$24 \div 6 =$ **4**
6.	$10 \times 7 =$ **70**	F	$27 \div 9 =$ **3**
7.	$6 \times 4 =$ **24**	G	$24 \div 3 =$ **8**
8.	$8 \times 8 =$ **64**	H	$36 \div 9 =$ **4**
9.	$3 \times 6 =$ **18**	I	$63 \div 7 =$ **9**
10.	$9 \times 4 =$ **36**	J	$18 \div 2 =$ **9**
11.	$9 \times 2 =$ **18**	K	$64 \div 8 =$ **8**
12.	$8 \times 3 =$ **24**	L	$70 \div 10 =$ **7**

Name____________________ Lesson 9.5

Fact Family Riddles

A fact family uses three numbers. Solve each riddle to find these three numbers. Then write the fact family for these numbers.

Remember the following vocabulary terms: ***dividend ÷ divisor = quotient***

1. Seven is the quotient. The dividend is a multiple of 4 that is less than 30.
   $7 \times 4 = 28$,
   $4 \times 7 = 28$,
   $28 \div 4 = 7$,
   $28 \div 7 = 4$

2. The quotient is 3 less than the divisor. The dividend is 18.
   $6 \times 3 = 18$,
   $3 \times 6 = 18$,
   $18 \div 3 = 6$,
   $18 \div 6 = 3$

3. This fact family contains two numbers that are less than 10. One of these numbers is equal to 3 times 3. When you multiply these two numbers together they equal a multiple of 5. Write the fact family.
   $9 \times 5 = 45$,
   $5 \times 9 = 45$,
   $45 \div 5 = 9$,
   $45 \div 9 = 5$

4. Both the quotient and divisor are equal numbers that are less than 5. The sum of the divisor and the quotient is 8. Write the fact family.
   $4 \times 4 = 16$;
   $16 \div 4 = 4$

Think About It!

5. How many number sentences did you write for exercise 4? How do you know this is correct?
   2; when both factors [or the divisor and quotient] are the same, there are only 2 number sentences in the fact family.

6. WRITE Math Write a riddle for the three numbers in a fact family. Then write the fact family for these numbers.
   Answers will vary but should describe 3 numbers that form 2 multiplication sentences and 2 division sentences.

Name________________ Lesson 9.6

Words and Numbers

Write the letter of the correct number sentence for each word problem. Then solve.

Word Problems

1. There are 9 pumpkins in a crate. There are 6 crates on a truck. How many pumpkins are on the truck?

   E; 54 pumpkins

2. Drew read 45 pages on Monday and 61 pages on Tuesday. How many pages did Drew read on Monday and Tuesday combined?

   D; 106 pages

3. Shoes cost $7 a pair. Lukas bought 3 pairs. How much money did Lukas spend in all?

   A; $21

4. Sally has 54 stickers. She gave the same number of stickers to 6 different friends. How many stickers did each friend receive?

   B; 9 stickers

5. Andre rode his bike 45 miles last week. Sasha rode her bike 61 miles last week. How many more miles did Sasha ride her bike last week than Andre rode his bike last week?

   C; 16 miles

Number Sentences

A. $\$7 \times 3 = ■$

B. $54 \div 6 = ■$

C. $61 - 45 = ■$

D. $45 + 61 = ■$

E. $9 \times 6 = ■$

Think About It!

6. WRITE Math Explain how writing a number sentence can help you to solve a word problem.

   Possible answer: Writing a number sentence helps me see how the numbers in a problem are related.

Name________________ Lesson 10.1

Color Division

1. Color in the boxes of any numbers that can be divided by 2 in the table below.

1	2	3	4	5	6	7	8	9	10
11	12	13	14	15	16	17	18	19	20

2. Color in the boxes of any numbers that can be divided by 5 in the table below.

1	2	3	4	5	6	7	8	9	10
11	12	13	14	15	16	17	18	19	20

3. Use the information from exercises 1 and 2 to complete the Venn diagram.

Numbers that can be divided by 2: **2, 4, 6, 8, 12, 14, 16, 18**

Both: **10, 20**

Numbers that can be divided by 5: **5, 15**

Think About It!

4. WRITE Math How did you decide which numbers to write in the overlap section of the Venn diagram?

   Possible Answer: I wrote the numbers that could be divided by 2 and 5.

5. **Stretch Your Thinking** Where would you place the number 30 in the Venn diagram? Explain.

   Possible Answer: I would place 30 in the overlap section because it has a 0 at the end, so it can be divided by both 2 and 5.

Name__________

Division Paint

Follow the directions below to color the picture. Shade any number that can:

- be divided only by 2: blue
- be divided only by 2 and 4: red
- be divided only by 3: yellow
- be divided only by 5: orange

2 and 14: blue
3, 9, 21, 24, 27: yellow
32, and 36: red
35, 45: orange

Think About It!

1. WRITE Math How did you decide when to shade a space green?

Possible answer: I tested each number with 2, 3, 4, and 5. If it worked for 2 or more of the numbers (except 2 and 4), I shaded it green.

2. **Stretch Your Thinking** Which color would you shade the number 30? Explain.

I would shade it green because 30 can be divided by 2, 3, and 5.

Name__________

Make the Number Sentence True

Write an operation sign (+, −, ×, ÷) to make each number sentence true.

1. $6 \oplus 6 = 12$
2. $0 \bigcirc 5 = 0$ **× or ÷**
3. $9 \bigcirc 1 = 9$ **× or ÷**
4. $4 \bigcirc 0 = 4$ **+ or −**
5. $1 \bigcirc (4 \div 4) = 1$ **× or ÷**
6. $(6 \otimes 0) \div 2 = 0$
7. $5 \oplus (20 \div 4) = 10$
8. $1 \times (5 \bigcirc 1) = 5$ **× or ÷**

Write a number in each box to make each number sentence true.

9. $5 \times (5 \div \boxed{5}) = 5$
10. $(3 \times \boxed{3}) \div 9 = 1$
11. $2 \times (\boxed{0} \div 4) = 0$
12. $4 \times (\boxed{7} + 1) = 32$
13. $\boxed{1} \times (4 \times 4) = 16$
14. $3 \times (\boxed{8} \div 4) = 6$
15. $(5 \times 5) \div \boxed{25} = 1$
16. $1 \times (0 \div \square) = 0$
any number except 0; possible answer: 8

Think About It!

17. WRITE Math Explain why two different operation symbols could be used for exercise 3.

Possible answer: 9 multiplied by 1 equals 9 and 9 divided by 1 equals 9.

18. **Stretch Your Thinking** Suppose you are given the number sentence:
$\square \div \square = 1.$
How would you describe the dividend and divisor?

Possible answer: The dividend and divisor must be the same number.

Name________________

Number Pair Bonanza

Draw a line to match each number pair with a description. Be careful, some descriptions may match more than one number pair, but there is only one way to match all of the pairs!

1. 0, 1 — The quotient is 5 and the sum is 24.
2. 20, 4 — The quotient is 1 and the difference is 0.
3. 2, 5 — The quotient is 6 less than the product.
4. 3, 3 — The product is 10 and the sum is 7.
5. 4, 1 — The product and quotient are both 0.
6. 25, 5 — The quotient is 5 and the difference is 4.
7. 2, 4 — The quotient is 5 less than the difference.
8. 12, 4 — The quotient is 5 and the difference is 20.
9. 1, 5 — The sum is 1 greater than the product.

Think About It!

10. WRITE Math Explain how you found the description for exercise 2.

Possible answer: I looked through all of the descriptions for a description that worked with the number pair.

11. **Stretch Your Thinking** Write your own description that could be used for the number pair in exercise 7.

Possible answer: The sum is 4 more than the quotient.

Name________________

What Should I Do?

Write the most appropriate operation from the table below, to answer each of the word problems following the table.

Multiply	Divide
Add	Subtract

1. I have 64 loaves of bread that need to be delivered evenly to 16 restaurants. Which operation should I use to make sure each restaurant receives the same number of bread loaves?

Divide

2. I have five dollars. My friend just asked me if he could have two dimes, but I just remembered I wanted to buy a magazine that costs $4.82. Which operation should I use to see if I can give him the money?

Subtract

3. A storeowner sold me 20 marbles for $1.60. My dad wanted to make sure that I received a good deal. He told me to figure out how much each marble had cost me. Which operation should I use to figure out the cost of each marble?

Divide

4. I noticed that from Monday to Tuesday the temperature rose 6 degrees. From Tuesday to Wednesday the temperature rose 19 degrees. From Wednesday to Sunday the temperature rose 23 degrees. Someone asked me to tell them how much the temperature had risen in that week. Which operation should I use to give them this answer?

Add

Think About It!

5. WRITE Math How did you know which operation to use in exercise 3? How much did each marble cost in exercise 3?

Possible answer; I realized that each marble costs a fraction of $1.60 so I divided. ;$0.08

6. Can the person in exercise 2 actually give his friend the money he wants, and still purchase the magazine he wants? Explain.

No; he would be short by 2 cents if he gave his friend the money.

Name____________________ **Lesson 11.1**

Division Puzzle

Find the missing dividends and quotients. Then use these clues to fill in the puzzle.

[1] 1	0	■	[2] 6	■	■	[3] 4
1	■	[4] 3	3	■	[5] 7	■
■	[6] 1	■	■	■	■	[7] 3
■	2	■	[8] 5	[9] 4	■	0
■	■	[10] 2	■	8	■	■

Across

1. 60 ÷ 6 = **10**
2. 36 ÷ 6 = **6**
3. 24 ÷ 6 = **4**
4. **33** ÷ 3 = 11
5. 42 ÷ 6 = **7**
8. **54** ÷ 6 = 9
10. 12 ÷ 6 = **2**

Down

1. 66 ÷ 6 = **11**
2. **63** ÷ 9 = 7
4. 18 ÷ 6 = **3**
6. 72 ÷ 6 = **10**
7. **30** ÷ 6 = 5
9. **48** ÷ 6 = 8

Think About It!

11. **Stretch Your Thinking** What if there was a 10 down. What number sentence could you write?

Sample answer:

2 ÷ 1 = 2

12. **Stretch Your Thinking** What if 2 across had to be a 2-digit number, with 6 in the tens column. What number sentence could you write?

Sample answer:

____ **÷ 8 = 8**

Name____________________ **Lesson 11.2**

Pieces of 8 (and 7)

Pieces of eight are old coins that were often stolen by pirates. You can find the missing pieces of 8 (and 7). Start with the divisor in the center of the treasure chest and work outward to fill in the missing dividends and quotients.

1\.

2\.

3\.

4\.

5\.

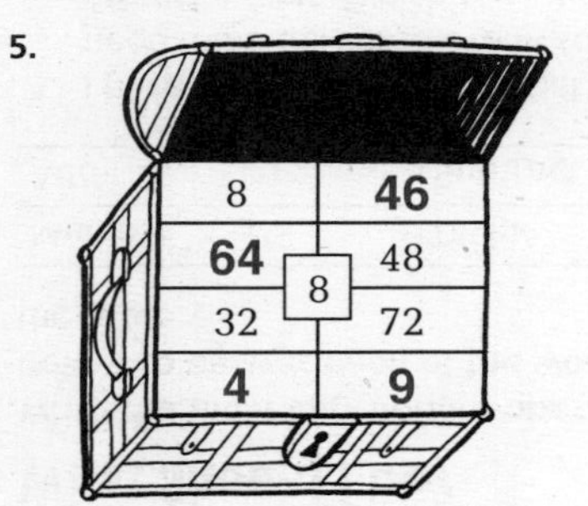

6\.

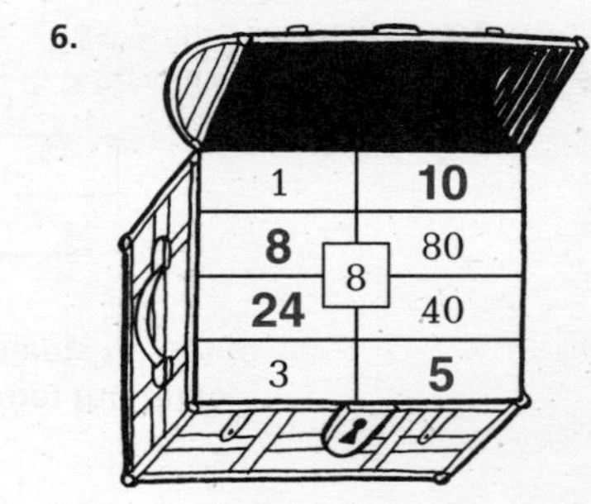

Name______________________

Working Backward to Find the Mystery Number

Read each number riddle. Use the clues to identify each number.

1. If you add 7 to me and then divide the sum by me, the answer is 8. What number am I?
   1
2. Multiply me by 5, the product is a number that is 5 more than 20. What number am I?
   5
3. Divide me by 3, or multiply me by 6. The answer will be the same. What number am I?
   0
4. When you multiply me by myself, the product is me again. What number am I?
   1 or 0
5. Divide 12 by 3, the quotient is me. Divide 12 by me, and you get 3. What number am I?
   4
6. If you multiply any number from 1–10 by me, the sum of the digits in the product equals me. What number am I?
   9
7. If you divide 30 by me, the quotient is 3 doubled. What number am I?
   5
8. If you divide any number by me, the quotient will be that number again. What number am I?
   1

Think About It!

9. WRITE Math How did you find the answer for exercise 4? Explain.
   Possible Answer; I knew that 1 and 0 are the only numbers when multiplied by themselves create the product of themselves.
10. **Stretch Your Thinking** Write your own number riddle for a number between 4 and 10 that has not already been used on this worksheet.
    Answers will vary

Name______________________

9 Balloon, 10 Balloon

You will need red and blue colored pencils, or crayons.

Use red to color every balloon showing a number that can be divided evenly by 9. Use blue to color every balloon showing a number that can be divided evenly by 10.

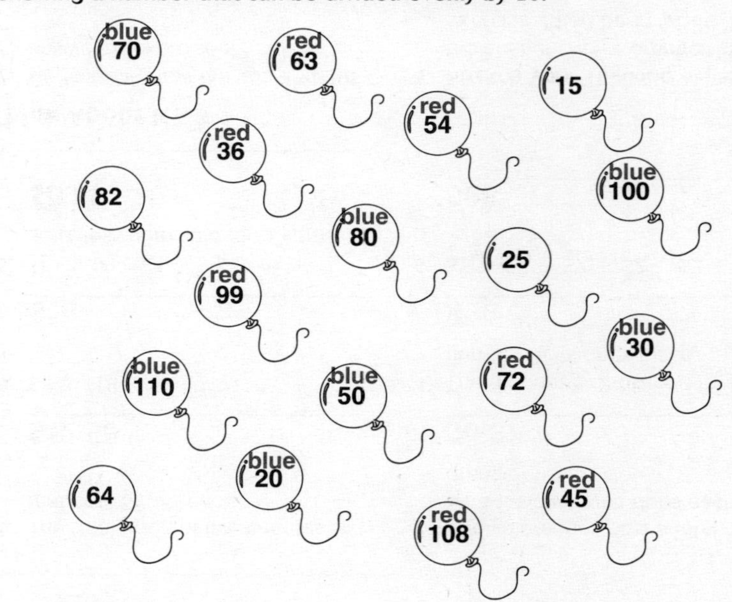

Think About It!

1. WRITE Math What do you notice about all the numbers that could be divided by 10? Explain.
   Possible Answer: The quotients are also divisible by 5.
2. **Stretch Your Thinking** Draw two more balloons showing numbers that can be divided by 9 and/or 10.
   Answers vary: 27, 60

Name______________________ Lesson 11.5

Check the Math

Sylvia answered incorrectly on some problems on her division homework. Check Sylvia's answers to the problems below. Find what Sylvia did incorrectly, and give the correct answer.

1. Write the multiplication and division fact family for 4, 6, 24.

   $4 \times 6 = 24$ $4 \div 6 = 24$
   $6 \times 4 = 24$ $6 \div 4 = 24$

   used incorrect dividend;
   $24 \div 6 = 4$, $24 \div 4 = 6$

2. Use repeated subtraction to solve $42 \div 7$.

   $42 - 6 = 36$ $36 - 6 = 30$
   $30 - 6 = 24$ $24 - 6 = 18$
   $18 - 6 = 12$ $12 - 6 = 6$
   $6 - 6 = 0$

   subtracted with 6 instead of 7;
   $42 - 7 = 35$, $35 - 7 = 28$,
   $28 - 7 = 21$, $21 - 7 = 14$,
   $14 - 7 = 7$, $7 - 7 = 0$

3. Jane has 35 stamps. She puts 5 stamps on each page of her book. How many pages does Jane use? Use counters to solve.

   grouped incorrectly;
   should be 5 groups of 7

4. Tyler ran 24 miles, evenly over 8 days. How many miles did Tyler run each day? Use counters to solve.

   grouped incorrectly;
   should be 3 groups of 8

Think About It!

5. **Stretch Your Thinking** Which other strategy could Sylvia have used to solve problem 3? Explain.
   Possible Answer: repeated subtraction

Name______________________ Lesson 11.6

Cost Match

Below is a grouping of prices. Fill these prices into the description that matches them. Use multiplication or division to help solve.

$36 $0.45 $12.50 $0.37 $16 $28

1. The total price of five candles that cost $2.50 each.
   $12.50

2. Twelve oranges cost a total of $4.44. How much does each orange cost?
   $0.37

3. $8 × (18 ÷ 9)
   $16

4. The amount $72 divided by the number in its ones place.
   $36

5. The total cost of 9 pieces of sugarless gum sold for 5 cents each.
   $0.45

6. $2 + $2 + $2 + $2 + $2 + $2 + $2 + $14
   $28

Think About It!

7. WRITE Math How did you find the answer to exercise 4?
   Possible Answer; I divided $72 by 2 since the number 2 is its ones place

8. **Stretch Your Thinking** What if the cost of twelve oranges in exercise 2 had been $4.80, how much would each orange cost then?
   $0.40

Name________________ Lesson 11.7

Writing Word Problems

Write a word problem to match each expression below. Then solve the problem showing the equation you used to solve.

Word problems will vary for 1–4; check students' work.

1. $54 \div 9$

   $54 \div 9 = 6$

2. $41 - 23$

   $41 - 23 = 18$

3. 8×3

   $8 \times 3 = 24$

4. $25 \div 5$

   $25 \div 5 = 5$

Think About It!

5. WRITE Math How does writing an equation help you solve a word problem? Explain.

   Sample answer: An equation helps me to organize the information from a word problem.

6. **Stretch Your Thinking** How would your word problem for exercise 4 be different if the expression had been 5×5?

   Possible answer: Instead of asking for the quotient, I would need to ask for the product.

Name________________ Lesson 12.1

Lines, Angles, Everywhere

Below are four figures. Look for line segments, right angles, angles less than right angles, and angles greater than right angles in each figure. List the terms that can help you describe each figure.

Figure	Terms
1.	line segments, greater than right angles
2.	line segments, less than right angles
3.	line segments less than right angles,
4.	the terms do not describe the circle

Think About It!

5. Which exercise had a figure without any line segments? Explain.

   exercise 4; a line segment is a straight part of a line with 2 end points, the figure in exercise 4 has no straight lines or end points

Stretch Your Thinking

6. If the figure in exercise 4 had been in the shape of a square, then how many of the figure, in exercises 1–4 would have line segments?

   4

Name________________ Lesson 12.2

Path of Lines

Following the clues to the treasure at the end of path.

Clues

1. Draw a line from the house to the picture with parallel lines under it.
2. Draw a line from the picture with parallel lines under it to the picture with the lines that intersect to form right angles under it.
3. Draw a line from the picture with the lines that intersect to from right angles under it to the picture with the intersecting lines under it.

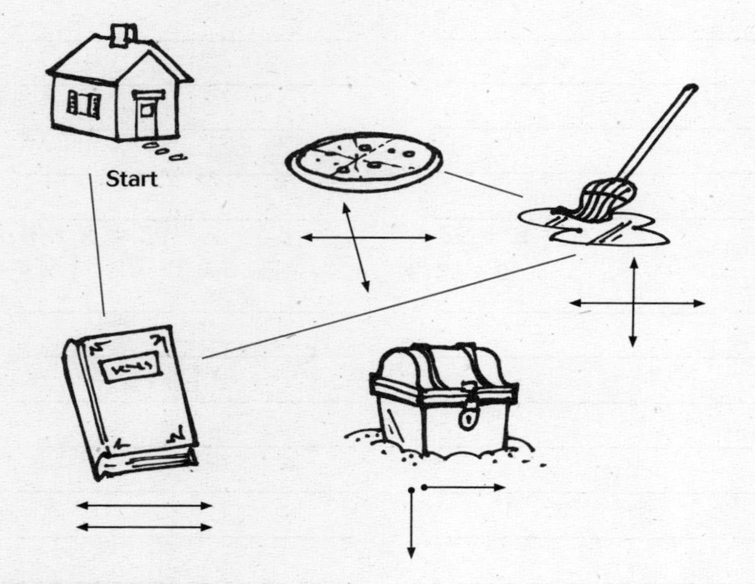

Think About It!

4. How did you know which picture represented the treasure?

The intersecting lines are under the pizza, rays are under the treasure chest

Name________________ Lesson 12.3

Polygon Puzzle

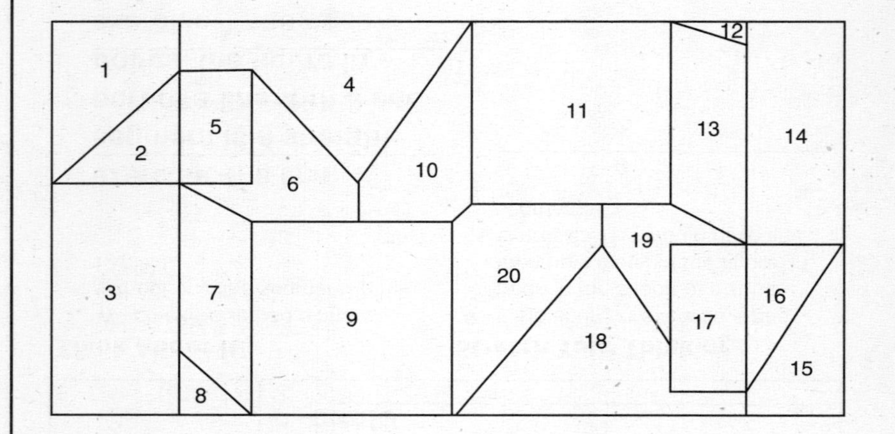

Follow the directions for the following exercises.

1. Write the numbers of the polygons that have only 4 sides and only 4 angles. 1, 5, 3, 7, 9, 11, 13, 14, 15, 17
2. Write the numbers of the polygons that have only 3 sides and only 3 angles. 2, 8, 12, 16
3. Write the numbers of the polygons that have 5 or more sides and 5 or more angles. 4, 6, 10, 18

Think About It!

Stretch Your Thinking What name would you give to figure 15? Explain.

Quadrilateral, it has 4 sides

Name________________ Lesson 12.4

The Triangular Spotted Frog

Tommy named the triangular spots on a frog in art class. He was supposed to have named them as in the list below. Did Tommy correctly or incorrectly name the spots on the frog.

List:

Triangle **A:** Isosceles
Triangle **B:** Equilateral
Triangle **C:** Scalene
Triangle **D:** Isosceles

3 cm, 3 cm, 3 cm (B); 2 cm, 2 cm, 1 cm (C); 3 cm, 4 cm, 1 cm (A); 1 cm, 4 cm, 4 cm (D)

1. Did Tommy name triangle A correctly? **no**
2. Did Tommy name triangle B correctly? **yes**
3. Did Tommy name triangle C correctly? **no**
4. Did Tommy name triangle D correctly? **yes**

Name________________ Lesson 12.5

Quadrilateral Riddles

Read the riddles below and decide what kind of figure is being described.

1. I am a quadrilateral with one pair of parallel sides. What figure am I? **trapezoid**
2. I am a parallelogram with 4 equal sides and 4 right angles. What figure am I? **square**
3. I am not a quadrilateral but I am a polygon. I have three sides. What figure am I? **triangle**
4. I am not a trapezoid, but I am a quadrilateral. I have 4 equal sides. I do not have 4 right angles. What figure am I? **rhombus**
5. I am a parallelogram with2 pairs of parallel sides,2 pairs of equal sides, and4 right angles. I am not a square. What figure am I? **rectangle**
6. I am a polygon with 4 sides and 4 angles. What figure am I? **quadrilateral**

Think About It!

7. WRITE Math How did you find the answer for exercise 1?

Possible Answer: A trapezoid is the only quadrilateral with only 1 pair of parallel sides

Stretch Your Thinking

8. WRITE Math How did you find the answer for exercise 6?

Possible Answer: a quadrilateral is the only normal polygon with 4 sides and 4 angles

Name________________ Lesson 12.6

Alike or Different Figures?

Below are five figures. Follow the instructions to draw a new figure.

1-5 Check students' figures.

Instructions	Figure	New Figure
1. Draw a new figure with the same number of sides as this one.		
2. Draw a new figure with the same number of angles as this one, but one that does not have a right angle.		
3. Draw a new figure that has the same number of parallel sides as this one.		
4. Draw a new figure that has at least one pair of parallel sides but a different number of parallel sides than this one.		
5. Draw a new figure that has the same types of angles as this one, but a different number of angles than this one.		

Think About It!

6. **Stretch Your Thinking** Below are two figures. How are these figures alike and different?

The triangles both have three sides and three angles. But the angles are different sizes.

Name________________ Lesson 12.7

What is Next?

Below are four patterns that have been started. Finish each pattern by adding in the next two figures or numbers in the sequence.

Pattern	Next 2 Numbers or Figures
50 45 40 35 30	1. 25 20
	2.
27, 33, 39, 45, 51	3. 57, 63
	4.

Think About It!

5. **Stretch Your Thinking** What are the next two numbers in this pattern:

20, 17, 14, 11, 8

5, 2

Stretch Your Thinking

6. What are the next two figures in this pattern:

○□□△○□□△○□

□△

Name

Solids Match Up

Draw lines to match the clues on the left with the correct solid figures on the right.

Clues	Solid Figures
1. I am a solid figure with 6 flat surfaces that are not all squares.	
2. I am a solid figure with 6 square-shaped flat surfaces.	
3. I am a solid figure shaped like a megaphone.	
4. I am a solid figure that you might find in the canned fruit aisle of the grocery store.	
5. I am a solid figure that can roll. I have no flat surfaces.	
6. I am a solid figure with 5 flat surfaces, 4 of which are triangular.	

Think About It!

7. Which solid figure does not belong? Explain.

Answers will vary. Possible answer: The cube doesn't belong because it has no curved surfaces.

8. WRITE Math Explain how these solid figures are different.

The triangular prism has triangular-shaped surfaces, the cube does not.

Name

Something is Missing

Use the clues in each of the following exercises to fill in the missing sections of the solid figures being described. Then tell which solid figure is being described.

1. 6 faces
   12 edges
   8 vertices

   Which solid figure is this?

   cube

2. 6 faces
   12 edges
   not a cube

   Which solid figure is this?

   rectangular prism

3. 5 faces
   9 edges
   6 vertices

   Which solid figure is this?

   triangular prism

4. 5 faces
   8 edges
   5 vertices

   Which solid figure is this?

   square pyramid

Think About It!

5. WRITE Math How did you arrive at an answer for exercise 2? Explain.

The other solid figure other than a cube that we learned about with 6 faces is a rectangular prism.

6. **Stretch Your Thinking** If exercise 4 had read: round surface, 0 edges, 0 vertices, and had not included a picture, then which solid figure would you think was being described?

Sphere. Cylinder and cone also acceptable.

Name________________ Lesson 13.3

Making the Figure

You can make solid figures with paper. Look at the patterns on this page.

- Copy the patterns onto grid paper.
- Cut the solid lines.
- Fold on the dotted lines.
- Use tape to hold your solid figure together.

What figures did you make? **cube, rectangular prism**

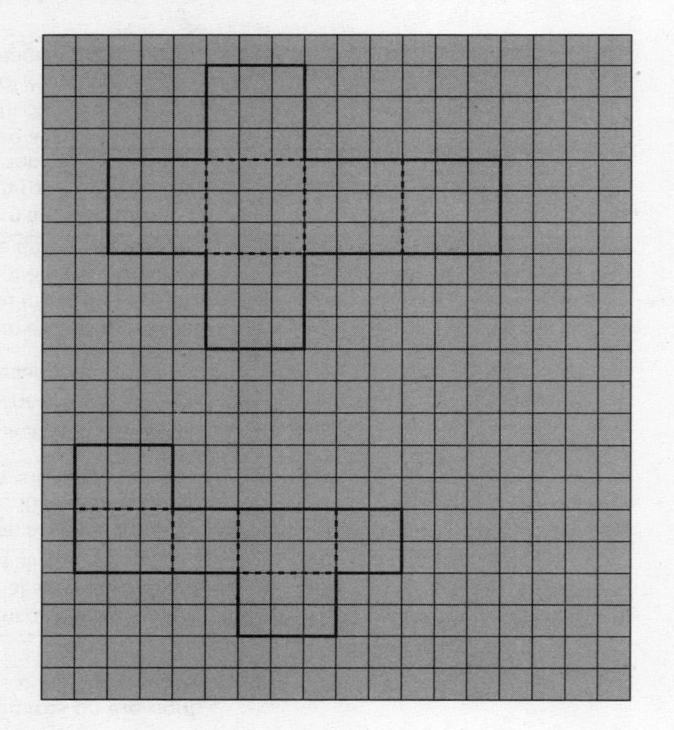

Name________________ Lesson 13.4

Solid Figure Combo

Draw each group of solid figures according to the directions given for each exercise. Make sure you understand each description before starting.

1. Draw a rectangular prism. Then draw a cube stacked on top of the rectangular prism. Finally, draw a cone stacked on top of the cube.

   Check students' drawings.

2. Draw two cubes placed next to each other so that together they form a rectangular prism. Then draw a square pyramid placed to the left of the cube. Finally, draw a cylinder placed to the right of the cube.

   Check students' drawings.

3. Draw a rectangular prism. Then draw two cylinders stacked, each resting on the rectangular prism. Finally, draw a rectangular prism stacked on top of the cylinders.

   Check students' drawings.

4. Draw a rectangular prism. Then draw a cylinder stacked on top of the prism in the middle. Finally, draw a cone on each side of the cylinder.

   Check students' drawings.

Think About It!

5. **Stretch Your Thinking** What is likely to happen if you place a rectangular prism on top of a square pyramid? Explain.

   Possible answer: The rectangular prism will not balance and will topple off the square pyramid.

Name________________ Lesson 13.5

In Plane View

Draw the top and bottom views for each figure.

Check students' drawings and patterns for 1-10

1. cylinder

circle, circle

2. rectangular prism

rectangle, rectangle

3. sphere

circle, circle

4. cube

square, square

Draw the bottom view for each figure.

5. cone

circle

6. square pyramid

square

Make a pattern using plane views of the given solid figures.

7. cylinder, cube, square pyramid

Answers will vary.

8. rectangular prism, cone, cylinder

Answers will vary.

9. square pyramid, cone

Answers will vary.

10. sphere, cube

Answers will vary.

Think About It!

11. WRITE Math What is the relationship between the bottom views of a rectangular prism and a triangular prism?

Possible Answer: The relationship between these bottom views is that they are the same, rectangular.

12. WRITE Math What is the relationship between the top views of a rectangular prism and a triangular prism?

Possible Answer: The relationship between these top views is that they are different. The rectangular prism has a rectangular top view and the triangular prism does not have a rectangular top view.

Name________________ Lesson 14.1

Perimeter Brainteaser

Read the following clues. Then write the name of each figure from greatest perimeter to least perimeter in the space provided. On each line, write the perimeter of the figure.

1. [ ] [ ] [ ] [ ]

_______ Units _______ Units _______ Units _______ Units

Figure A:

a. I am the largest figure of all. My perimeter is greater than 20 units.

b. All of my sides are the same length.

Figure B:

a. The length of one of my sides is 2.

b. All of my sides are the same length.

Figure C:

a. My perimeter is less than the perimeter of Figure D.

b. Two of my sides are each 8 units long.

c. Two of my sides are each 1 unit long.

Figure D:

a. My perimeter is 4 less than Figure A.

b. Two of my sides are each 6 units long.

c. Two of my sides are each 4 units long.

The boxes in order from greatest perimeter to least perimeter: Figure A (24 units), Figure D (20 units), Figure C (18 units), Figure B (8 units).

Think About It!

2. Lance has a rectangle that is twice as long as it is wide. One side of the rectangle is 2 units. The perimeter is greater than 6 units but less than 14 units. What is the perimeter of Lance's rectangle?

12 units.

3. Ernesto has a square that has a perimeter greater than 20 units and less than 28 units. The length of each side is an even number. What is the perimeter of Ernesto's square?

24 units.

Name________________

Mystery Perimeter

Test your estimation skills.

1. One of the four figures below has a perimeter that measures 12 centimeters. Guess which figure and write your answer on the line below.

   Answers will vary.

2. Use a centimeter ruler to measure each figure. Write the name of the figure with a perimeter that measures 12 centimeters in the box below.

   Figure B

Figure A:

Figure B:

Figure C:

Figure D:

Think About It!

3. **Stretch Your Thinking** Draw a picture of a triangle with a perimeter that measures 12 centimeters. Label the length of each side.

   Check students' drawings. Possible answer: an equilateral triangle with sides that each measure, and are labeled, 4 centimeters.

4. **Stretch Your Thinking** Draw a picture of a square with a perimeter that measures 12 centimeters. Label the length of each side.

   Check students' drawings. A square with sides that each measure, and are labeled, 3 centimeters

Name________________

Area – Follow the Clues!

Use the clues to answer the riddles below.

1. **a.** I am a rectangle.
   b. The length of my longer sides both measure 5 units.
   c. My area is 20 square units.

   What is the length of each of my shorter sides?

   4 units

2. **a.** I am a rectangle.
   b. Two of my sides are 3 units long.
   c. My area is 20 square units

   What is the length of my other sides?

   6 units

3. **a.** I am a square.
   b. One of my sides is 8 units long.

   What is my area?

   64 square units

4. **a.** I am a square.
   b. My area is 16 square units.

   What is the length of one of my sides?

   4 units

5. **a.** I am a rectangle.
   b. One of my sides is 6 units long.
   c. One of my sides is 5 units long.

   What is my area?

   30 square units

6. **a.** I am a rectangle.
   b. The length of each of my shorter sides is 2 units.
   c. My area is 14 square units.

   What is the length of one of my longer sides?

   7 units

Think About It!

7. **Write Math** How did you find the answer for exercise 4?

   I divided 16 by 4.

8. **Stretch You Thinking** Read the clues. Circle the rectangle being described.
   a. My perimeter is 18 units.
   b. My area is less than 20 square units.
   c. My longer side is twice the length of my shorter side.

   Figure B

7 units
A
2 units
3 units
B
6 units

Name____________________

Area of Solid Figures Bungle

For each exercise below, faces of solid figures are separated and shown with the number of units per face labeled upon them. The face with student handwriting is incorrectly labeled. Use the area of the solid figures and the area of the other faces to decide what the student written data should have been.

1. 7 units | 7 units | 7 units | 7 units | 7 units | 6 units ____ **7 units**

   Area of Solid Figures: 42 units

2. 10 units | 12 units ____ **8 units** | 8 units

   Area of Solid Figures: 26 units

3. 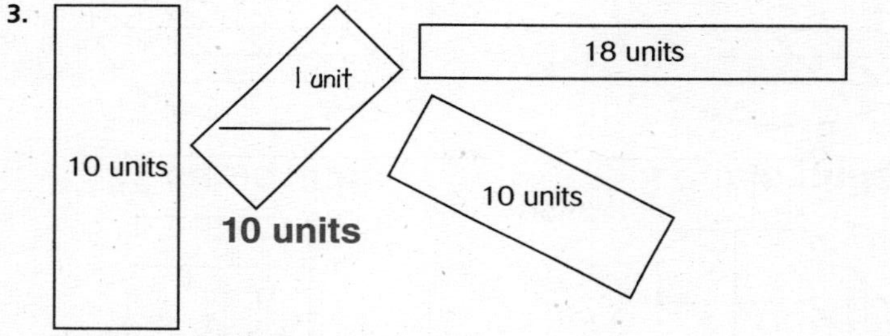

   Area of Solid Figures: 48 units

Think About It!

5. **Stretch Your Thinking** If the student written label for exercise 3 had read 12 units, but the plane figure that currently reads 18 units had read 9 units, would the figures add up to the correct area of 48 units? Explain.

   Possible answer: No; it would still be short by 7 units under the actual area.

Name____________________

Less Than Complete

Fill in the missing information in the following scenarios to make each scenario correct.

1. Each layer of a prism is 8 cubic units. The volume is **48** cubic units. There are 6 layers in the prism.
2. Each layer of a prism is **4** cubic units. The volume is 24 cubic units. There are 6 layers in the prism.
3. Each **layer** of a prism is 4 cubic units. The volume is 12 cubic units. There are 3 layers in the prism.
4. Each layer of a prism is 10 cubic units. The **volume** is 40 cubic units. There are 4 layers in the prism.
5. Each layer of a prism is 8 cubic units. The volume is **32** cubic units. There are 4 layers in the prism.
6. Each layer of a prism is 2 cubic units. The volume is 2 cubic units. There is **one** layer in the prism.
7. Each layer of a prism is 12 cubic units. The volume is **36** cubic units. There are 3 layers in the prism.
8. Each layer of a prism is 4 cubic units. The volume is 16 cubic units. There are **4** layers in the prism.

Think About It!

6. WRITE Math How did you find the missing information for exercise 4?

   Possible answer: I looked at the number of layers, cubic units per layer, and knew 40 referred to volume.

7. WRITE Math How did you find the missing information for exercise 7?

   Possible answer: I multiplied the number of cubic units in one layer by the number of layers.

Name____________________

Lesson 14.6

Volume Control

Emily has 50 cubic units to place in 3 of the 4 boxes below so that there are no cubic units left over. Below each box, write the number of cubic units it will hold. Then circle the 3 boxes Emily should use.

1.

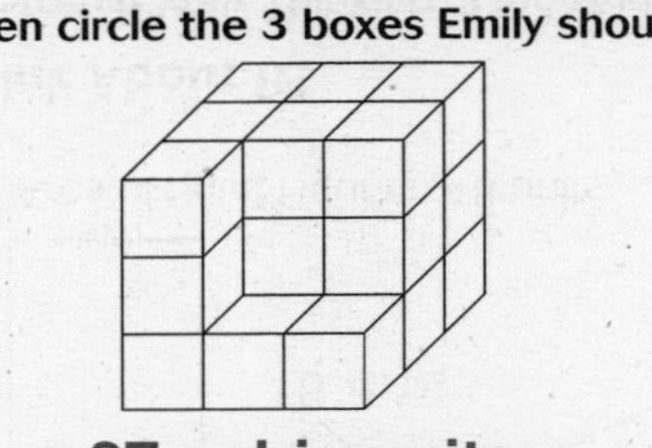

27 cubic units

2.

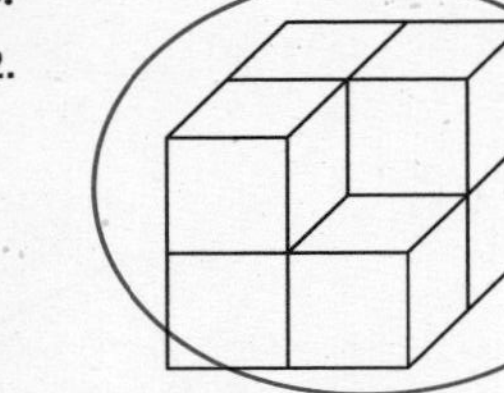

8 cubic units

3.

24 cubic units

4.

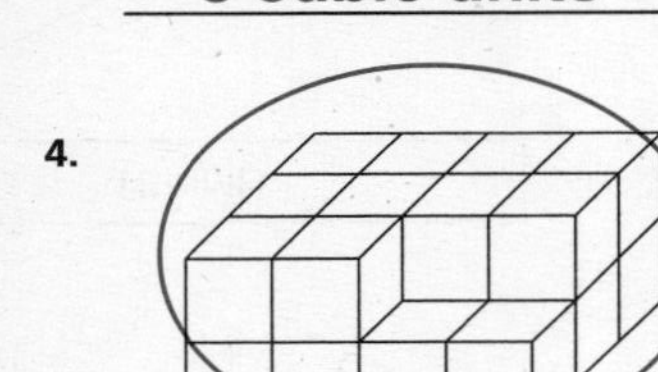

18 cubic units

Think About It!

5. **Stretch Your Thinking** Elizabeth wants to pack 15 pencil boxes into a carton so that there are either 2, or 3, identical layers. Should Elizabeth place the pencil boxes in 2, or 3, identical layers? Why?

Possible explanation: She must stack the pencil boxes in 3 identical layers with 5 boxes in each layer. She cannot stack 15 boxes in 2 identical layers because there will be 1 box left over.

Name____________________

Lesson 15.1

Pattern Facts

Circle the expression you can use to find the product given in the solar system fact.

1. Pluto is classified as a dwarf planet. Pluto has a diameter of about 1,500 miles, which is smaller than Earth's moon!

   3 × 5   3 × 50   (30 × 50)   30 × 500

2. The largest planet in our solar system is Jupiter, which has a diameter of about 88,000 miles.

   (11 × 8,000)   110 × 8,000   11 × 800   110 × 80

3. Mercury is the fastest orbiting planet in the solar system. It only takes about 90 days to orbit the Sun.

   9 × 1   (9 × 10)   90 × 10   90 × 100

4. Neptune has a diameter of about 30,000 miles.

   50 × 60   500 × 6,000   500 × 600   (50 × 600)

5. Mercury takes about 4,200 hours to rotate once on its axis.

   60 × 7   (60 × 70)   60 × 700   60 × 7,000

6. Mount Olympus, on Mars, is about 80,000 feet tall.

   (8,000 × 10)   8,000 × 100   800 × 10   800 × 1,000

7. Earth is the third planet from the Sun. Earth's diameter is about 8,000 miles.

   400 × 20   4,000 × 20   400 × 20   400 × 2

Think About It!

1. **Stretch Your Thinking** The Sun's diameter is about 100 times greater than the Earth's diameter. What is the approximate diameter of the Sun? (**HINT:** Earth's diameter is given in Problem 7.)

   About 800,000 miles

2. WRITE Math Explain how you decided which expression represented the product shown in each solar system fact.

   Possible answer: I used basic facts and patterns to find the expression with the value shown in the solar system fact.

Name

Arrray of Cars

Color in the following giant array of cars by creating smaller arrays based on the equations in the box below.

3 × 12; color blue	4 × 18; color yellow
2 × 11; color gray	5 × 22; color black

Think About It

1. How did multiplying by 10 and 1 help you color in your arrays?

Possible Answer: I separated the two digits factors into tens and ones then multiplied and added to find the product

Name

Vacant Products

Write the missing numbers.

1. 39 × 7 = 2□3 **7**
2. 53 × 5 = □65 **2**
3. 46 × 4 = 18□ **4**
4. 28 × □ = 168 **6**
5. 72 × □ = 432 **6**
6. 82 × □ = 738 **9**
7. 3□ × 5 = 180 **6**
8. □2 × 9 = 828 **9**
9. 2□ × 4 = 116 **9**
10. □ × 15 = 105 **7**
11. 5 × □ = 125 **25**
12. 6 × 33 = □ **198**

Find the error. Explain.

13. 7 × 1 ten = 7
Product s/b 70; 1 ten is 10

14. 8 × 3 tens = 24
Product s/b 240; 3 tens are 30

15. 6 × 2 tens = 12
Product s/b 120; 2 tens are 20

Think About It

16. WRITE Math How did you find the missing number in excercise 10?

Possible Answer: trial and error with the factor until I realized 7 × 15 = 105

17. WRITE Math How did you find the error number in excercise 13?

Possible Answer: I knew that 7 × 1 ten was a much greater product than 7

EW87-EW88

Name____________________ Lesson 15.4

Estimation Tint

Look at each problem below. If the answer product is an estimate then shade the box..

77 × 5 = 400 (shaded)	920 × 2 = 1,840	17 × 5 = 100 (shaded)
68 × 3 = 204	431 × 6 = 2,586	573 × 2 = 1,146
61 × 8 = 480 (shaded)	563 × 3 = 1,689	749 × 7 = 4,900 (shaded)
920 × 6 = 5,400 (shaded)	47 × 9 = 423	313 × 4 = 1,200 (shaded)
230 × 7 = 1,610	138 × 9 = 900 (shaded)	639 × 6 = 3,834
493 × 4 = 1,972	897 × 4 = 3,600 (shaded)	724 × 9 = 6,516
217 × 6 = 1,302	542 × 7 = 3,794	386 × 5 = 1,930
497 × 5 = 2,500 (shaded)	617 × 8 = 4,936	218 × 4 = 800 (shaded)

Name____________________ Lesson 15.5

So True

Fill in the missing number of tens to make the number sentence true.

1. $5 \times \square$ tens $= 450$ **9**
2. $7 \times \square$ tens $= 490$ **7**
3. $8 \times \square$ tens $= 640$ **8**
4. $9 \times \square$ tens $= 810$ **9**
5. $6 \times \square$ tens $+ 8 = 308$ **5**
6. $9 \times \square$ tens $+ 6 = 276$ **3**
7. $4 \times \square$ tens $+ 14 = 254$ **6**
8. $3 \times \square$ tens $+ 23 = 233$ **7**
9. $2 \times \square$ tens $- 7 = 153$ **8**
10. $7 \times \square$ tens $- 11 = 549$ **8**

Think About It

11. WRITE Math How did you find the missing number of tens for excercise 10?

Possible Answers: I 1st added 11 to 549 to get 560, then I predicted and tested factors until I needed 8 tens

12. **Stretch your Thinking** If a problem read □ tens × □ tens = 811 could you fill in the missing numbers to reach the product? Explain.

Possible Answers: No: a group of tens times another group of tens will always result in a product ending in zero

Name______________________ Lesson 15.6

Image Solutions

Draw pictures to demonstrate each problem. Then solve. The first one is started for you.

1. The corner store sells yogurt. A small yogurt costs \$1.25. A medium yogurt costs \$1.75. A large yogurt costs \$2.15. In one hour the store sells 5 small yogurts, 7 medium yogurts and 8 large yogurts. How much money does the corner store make during 1 hour?

   \$35.70; check student drawings

2. Marilyn's brother needs to read 3 books. Each book has 588 pages. How many pages must he read?

   1,764 pages; check student drawings

Think About It

3. WRITE Math How did drawing the pictures help solve the problems.

   Possible Answer: I could group the pictures together to solve simple problems and then use each grouping to solve the overall problem

4. Lilly earns \$8.00 a week. She spends \$0.50 on each of 5 days on school lunches. She buys a treat on Saturdays for \$1.20. She saves the rest of her money. How much does Lilly save in 4 weeks?

   \$17.20

Name______________________ Lesson 16.1

Missing Multiples

Each of the two sets of number sentences below have four different patterns, the same factor is missing from each pattern in the set. Write the missing factor in the circle for each set.

Set 1

$30{,}000 = 6{,}000 \times$ ____ ____ $\times 3{,}000 = 15{,}000$
$3{,}000 = 600 \times$ ____ ____ $\times 300 = 1{,}500$
$300 = 60 \times$ ____ ____ $\times 30 = 150$
$30 = 6 \times$ ____ ____ $\times 3 = 15$

5

$40 = 8 \times$ ____ ____ $\times 7 = 35$
$400 = 80 \times$ ____ ____ $\times 70 = 350$
$4{,}000 = 800 \times$ ____ ____ $\times 700 = 3{,}500$
$40{,}000 = 8{,}000 \times$ ____ ____ $\times 7{,}000 = 35{,}000$

Set 2

$63{,}000 = 9{,}000 \times$ ____ ____ $\times 4{,}000 = 28{,}000$
$6{,}300 = 900 \times$ ____ ____ $\times 400 = 2{,}800$
$630 = 90 \times$ ____ ____ $\times 40 = 280$
$63 = 9 \times$ ____ ____ $\times 4 = 28$

7

$42 = 6 \times$ ____ ____ $\times 5 = 35$
$420 = 60 \times$ ____ ____ $\times 50 = 350$
$4{,}200 = 600 \times$ ____ ____ $\times 500 = 3{,}500$
$42{,}000 = 6{,}000 \times$ ____ ____ $\times 5{,}000 = 35{,}000$

Think About It!

1. WRITE Math How did you find the missing multiple for the first set?

   Possible Answer: I found the most basic facts first $30 = 6 \times$ ___, ___ $\times 3 = 15$ $40 = 8 \times$ ___, etc and then checked for the other ones to make sure 5 worked

2. **Stretch Your Thinking** If the bottom row of set 2 had read $42{,}000 = 5{,}000 \times$ ___ and ___ $\times 6{,}000 = 35{,}000$ would the missing multiple remain the same? Explain.

   Possible Answer: No, 5,000 does not go evenly into 42,000 nor does 6,000 go evenly into 35,000

Name______________________ Lesson 16.2

The Museum Mystery

Fill in the missing information for the word problems below.!

1. A museum has __6__ floors. Each floor has 7 exhibits. Each exhibit has 100 paintings on the wall. There are 4,200 paintings on the walls of the museum in all.

2. A museum has 5 floors. Between each floor there are 25 stairs. There are __100__ stairs between the floors of the museum in all. The museum has locations in 24 other cities.There are a total of 2,500 stairs between the floors of all of these locations combined.

3. At the end of a convention there were 4 exhibits missing from a museum. Extra guards were called in to guard the other 116 exhibits. A total of __464__ guards how guarded 116 exhibits evenly. If all the exhibits had been there and the museum still wanted to guard them evenly with the same numbers of guards per exhibit, they would have needed 480 guards.

4. A museum has 3 guards for each floor. There are 30 guards in the whole building. Each guard visits 10 exhibits each night. The three guards per floor visit all of the exhibits on that floor each night. There are __300__ exhibits in the museum in all.

Think About It.

5. WRITE Math How did you find the answer for exercise 1?

Possible Answer:
I multiplied 700 times
6 to test if the product
would be 4200

6. WRITE Math How did you find the answer for exercise 2?

Possible Answer:
I multiplied 25 times
4 since there are only
4 between portions
within 5 floors

Name______________________ Lesson 16.3

3-Digit Number Riddles

Solve each riddle.

1. I am a 3-digit number. When you multiply me by 7, the product is 2,275. What number am I?

   325

2. I am a 1-digit number. When you multiply me by 284, the product is 1,704. What number am I?

   6

3. I am a 1-digit number. When you multiply me by 298, the last 2 digits in the product are 8. What number am I?

   6

4. I am a 3-digit number. When you multiply me by 8, the product is, 3,608. What number am I?

   451

5. I am a 1-digit number. When you multiply me by 355, the product is still a 1-digit number. What number am I?

   0

6. I am a 1-digit number. When you multiply me by 458, the product is 3,206. What number am I?

   7

7. I am a 3-digit number. When you multiply me by 7, the product is 153 less than 1,000. What number am I?

   121

8. I am a 2-digit number. When you multiply me by 9 the product is 891. What number am I?

   99

Think About It

9. WRITE Math How did you find the answer for excercise 7?

Possible Answer: I
subtracted 153 from
1,000 to reach 847
then tested
multiplying 3 digit
numbers ending in 1

10. If 10 was added to the factor 458 and the product 3,206 in excercise 6, would a 1-digit number still solve the riddle? Explain

Possible Answer: No
468 cannot be
multiplied by any
1-digit to reach 3216

Name________________ Lesson 16.4

You Check the Math!

Write the missing numbers.

1. 3,291 × 7 = 2 [3] ,037
2. 5,335 × 5 = [2] 6,675
3. 4,611 × 4 = 18, [4] 44
4. 2,832 × [5] = 14,160
5. 7,224 × [6] = 43,344
6. 8,255 × [8] = 66,040
7. 3, [6] 80 × 5 = 18,400
8. 1,7 [9] 2 × 9 = 16,128
9. 3,42 [9] × 4 = 13,716
10. [7] × 1,568 = 10,976
11. 5 × [ ] = 12,500 **2,500**
12. 6 × 3,323 = [ ] **19,938**

Find the errors.

13. 4,562 × 3 = 12,586 (regrouped 1 1)

The regrouped hundred and thousand were not added.

14. 4,831 × 5 = 24,055 (regrouped 4 1)

The regrouped hundred was not added.

15. 7,551 × 2 = 14,102 (regrouped 1 1)

The regrouped thousand was not added.

Think About It

16. WRITE Math How did you find the error in exercise 14? Explain.

Possible Answer: The regrouped hundred was not added.

17. **Stretch Your Thinking** Circle the error in the problem: 4,881 × 5 = 244,05 (regrouped 4 4; 0 written in)

Name________________ Lesson 16.5

Error Alert Money

In each of the following problems, Brian was told to multiply money amounts like whole numbers. Circle any mistakes Brian made during his work. Then write the correct product.

1. Multiply: $7.42 × 4

Brian's Work: 7.42 × 4 = ($)29.68

Correct Product: **$ 29.68**

2. Multiply: $0.63 ×8

Brian's Work: 63 ×8 = 5.04

Correct Product: **$ 5.04**

3. Multiply: $18.00 × 2

Brian's Work: 1800 × 2 = ($)3.600

Correct Product: **$36.00**

4. Multiply: $5.55 × 5

Brian's Work: 555 × 5 = 27.75

Correct Product: **$27.75**

Think About It

5. WRITE Math How are the errors in exercises 1 and 4 alike?

Possible Answer: Both of Brian's products had one to many decimal points

6. WRITE Math How are the errors in exercises 2 and 4 different?

Possible Answer: Although both are missing a doller sign Brian only added an extra point to his product in exercise 4 not 2

Name__________

Dividing Gardens

Thomas, David, Michelle, and Allison are each going to plant a flower garden. They will plant their flowers in rows. Read how many flowers and rows will be in each garden. Draw a model to help you determine how many flowers will be in each row.

1. Thomas has 42 flowers. He plants them evenly in 6 rows. How many flowers does Thomas have in each row? **7 flowers**

2. David has 30 flowers. He plants them evenly in 5 rows. How many flowers does David have in each row? **6 flowers**

3. Michelle has 72 flowers. She plants them evenly in 8 rows. How many flowers does Michelle have in each row? **9 flowers**

4. Allison has 24 flowers. She plants them evenly in 3 rows. How many flowers does Allison have in each row? **8 flowers**

Think About It!

5. **Stretch Your Thinking** You decide to plant a garden. Write a new problem to tell how many flowers and rows you will have in your garden.
Answers will vary. Check for accuracy.

6. WRITE Math How can you check each answer for exercises 1–4?
Multiply the number of flowers in each row by the number of rows to see if this matches the total number of flowers.

Name__________

Dividing the Treasure

Draw lines to match the basic facts on the left hand side of the page with the division problems that pirates are using to divide the jewels with on the right hand side of the page

1. $24 \div 4 = 6$
2. $56 \div 4 = 8$
3. $8 \div 4 = 2$
4. $20 \div 4 = 5$

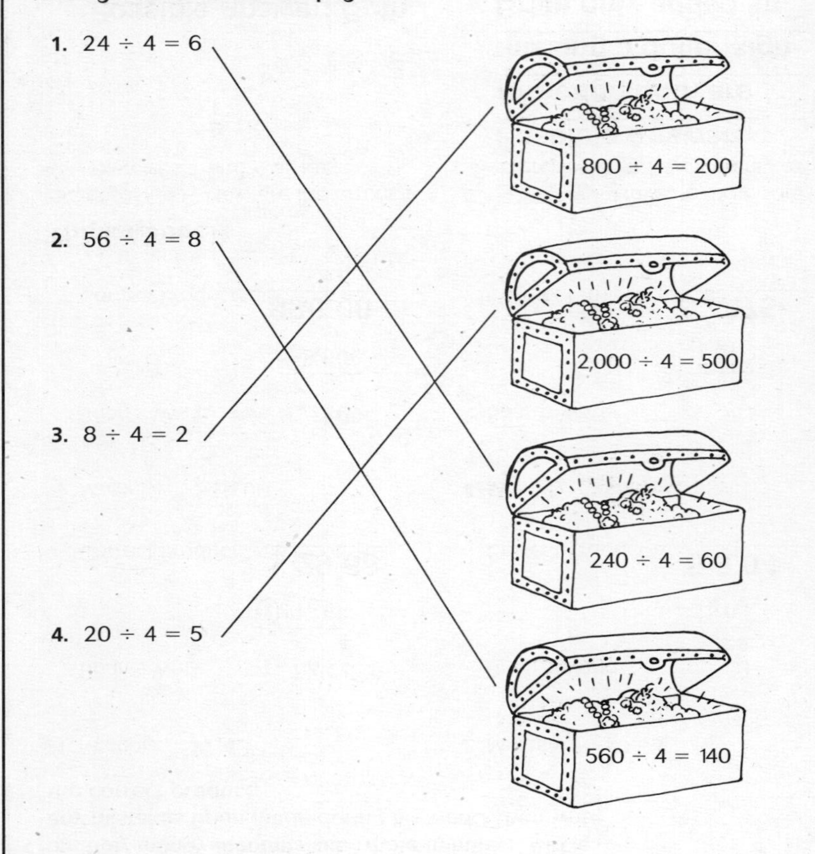

Name______________________ Lesson 17.3

Amusement Park Estimation

Funland Amusement Park recorded the number of people who took part in specific attractions. Look at the chart and use compatible numbers to help you solve the problems.

Amusement Park Attractions	
Attractions	Number of People Who took part in Attractions
Roller Coaster	350
Fun House	418
Log Ride	234
Swings	119

1. If 4 people can fit it one car on the roller coaster. About how many cars did it take for everyone to ride?
   about 90 cars

2. The Fun House can have 6 people in at one time. About how many groups of 6 people went through the Fun House?
   about 70 groups

3. Only 3 people can fit in one boat on the log ride. About how many boats did it take for everyone to ride?
   about 80 boats

4. Each set of swings holds 2 people. About how many sets of swings did it take for everyone to ride?
   about 60

Think About It!

5. **Stretch Your Thinking** Choose a new ride and add it to the chart. Decide how many people will ride. Then create a new problem using this information.
   Answers will vary. Check for accuracy.

6. WRITE Math How can using compatible numbers help you estimate quotients?
   It helps when a problem doesn't need an exact answer. Using numbers that are easy to divide helps solve the problem.

Name______________________ Lesson 17.4

Riddle Division

Find the quotient for each problem. Then write the letter from each box on the line above the matching number. Use multiplication to check your answer.

What do dogs and trees have in common?

Problem	Quotient	Letter
$6\overline{)204}$	34	O
$9\overline{)189}$	21	T
$7\overline{)336}$	48	A
$9\overline{)630}$	70	H
$8\overline{)760}$	95	Y
$8\overline{)104}$	13	V
$6\overline{)402}$	67	B
$5\overline{)415}$	83	E
$5\overline{)395}$	79	K
$3\overline{)168}$	56	R

T H E Y   B O T H   H A V E   B A R K

21 70 83 95   67 34 21 70   70 48 13 83   67 48 56 79

EW99-EW100

Name____________________ Lesson 17.5

Not Quite Complete

Tony began working out the following problems using the "Solve a Simpler Problem" strategy. Tony showed part of his work and showed his answer. Fill in the missing work.

1. Jan takes swimming lessons. Her first payment was $42. This included a $5 registration fee, $10 for insurance, and 3 weeks of lessons. How much did Jan pay for each week of lessons?

   Tony's Work: $10 + $5 = $15
   $42 − $15 = $27

   Tony's Answer: $9 per week
   Missing Work: **$27 ÷ 3 = $9**

2. Sadine takes fencing lessons. Her first payment was $67. This included a $7 registration fee, $14 for insurance, and 2 weeks of lessons. How much did Sadine pay for each week of lessons?

   Tony's Work: $7 + $14 = $21
   $67 − $21 = $27

   Tony's Answer: $23 per week
   Missing Work: **$46 ÷ 2 = $23**

3. Paul decides to keep track of the naps he takes each week. The first week he took 5 naps, the second week he took 8 naps, and the third week he took 8 naps. How many naps did Paul average per week?

   Tony's Work: 5 + 8 + 8 = 21

   Tony's Answer: 7 naps per week
   Missing Work: **21 ÷ 3 = 7**

4. Erica takes ballet lessons. Her first payment was $75. This included a $5 registration fee, $10 for insurance, and 5 weeks of lessons. How much did Erica pay for each week of lessons?

   Tony's Work: $5 + $10 = $15
   $75 − $15 = $60

   Tony's Answer: $12 per week
   Missing Work: **$60 ÷ 5 = $12**

Think About It!

5. WRITE Math How did you find the missing work for exercise 3?

   Possible Answer: I knew that he should have divided 21 by 3 weeks

Name____________________ Lesson 17.6

Picture Quotient

Divide money amounts. Connect the dots in order from least to greatest quotient.

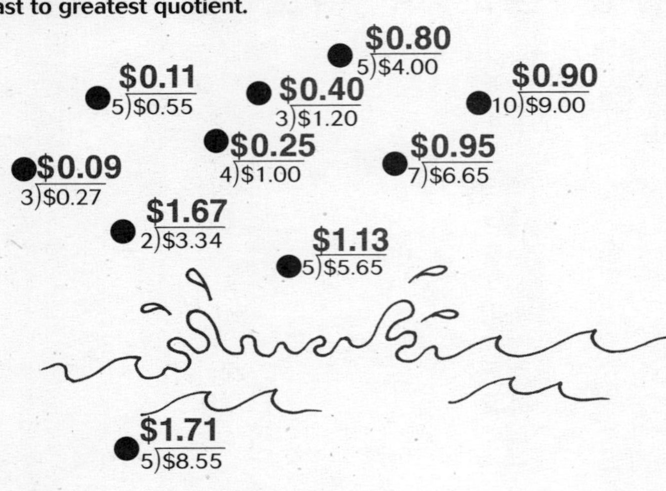

Think About It!

1. What shape did the dots create?

   Possible Answer; dolphin, whale, porpoise

Name____________________ Lesson 17.7

The Remaining Basketballs

Rachel, Samuel, Courtney, Linda, and Jonathan went to the park to play. At the playground they found 23 basketballs to use for practice shots. Draw a picture to show how to divide the balls equally between the 5 friends. Draw a picture to show the remaining balls.

Rachel	Samuel
Courtney	Linda
Jonathan	**4 balls each Remaining balls: 3 balls Remaining basketballs**

Think About It!

1. **Stretch Your Thinking** Imagine that Courtney finds 6 more basketballs behind the slide. How many basketballs will each friend have now? How many basketballs will be left over?

   5 balls each; 5 balls remaining

2. WRITE Math Why are there remaining basketballs.

   There is a remainder because the balls can not be divided into equal groups.

Name____________________ Lesson 18.1

Pizza Fraction

Decide if the student answers to the following problems are correct or incorrect. Write correct or incorrect on the line. If the student's answer is incorrect, write the correct answer

1. Josie took two slices of pizza from a 12-slice pizza pie. How much of the pizza pie is left?

   Student Answer: $\frac{1}{2}$ of the pizza pie

   incorrect; $\frac{5}{6}$ of the pizza pie

2. Sherry took three slices of pizza from a 12-slice pizza pie. How much of the pizza pie is left?

   Student Answer: $\frac{1}{4}$ of the pizza pie

   incorrect; $\frac{3}{4}$ of the pizza pie

3. Sigmund took 7 slices of pizza from a 14-slice pizza pie. How much of the pizza pie is left?

   Student Answer: $\frac{1}{2}$ of the pizza pie

   correct

4. Jim took three slices of pizza from a 6-slice pizza pie. How much of the pizza pie is left?

   Student Answer: $\frac{3}{4}$ of the pizza pie

   incorrect; $\frac{1}{2}$ of the pizza pie

5. Horace took two slices of pizza from a 10-slice pizza pie. How much of the pizza pie is left?

   Student Answer: $\frac{4}{5}$ of the pizza pie

   correct

6. Leslie took one slice of pizza from a 6-slice pizza pie. How much of the pizza pie is left?

   Student Answer: $\frac{1}{3}$ of the pizza pie

   incorrect; $\frac{5}{6}$ of the pizza pie

Think About It!

7. WRITE Math How did you find the answer for exercise 6?

   Possible answer: I know that there was 5/6 of the pizza left so it was incorrect

8. **Stretch Your Thinking** How many slices of pizza could Leslie have taken to change your answer for exercise 6?

   4 slices

Name____________________

Funny Macaroni!

Kevin and Tim each have a bag full of colored macaroni. Use the pictures below to answer the questions.

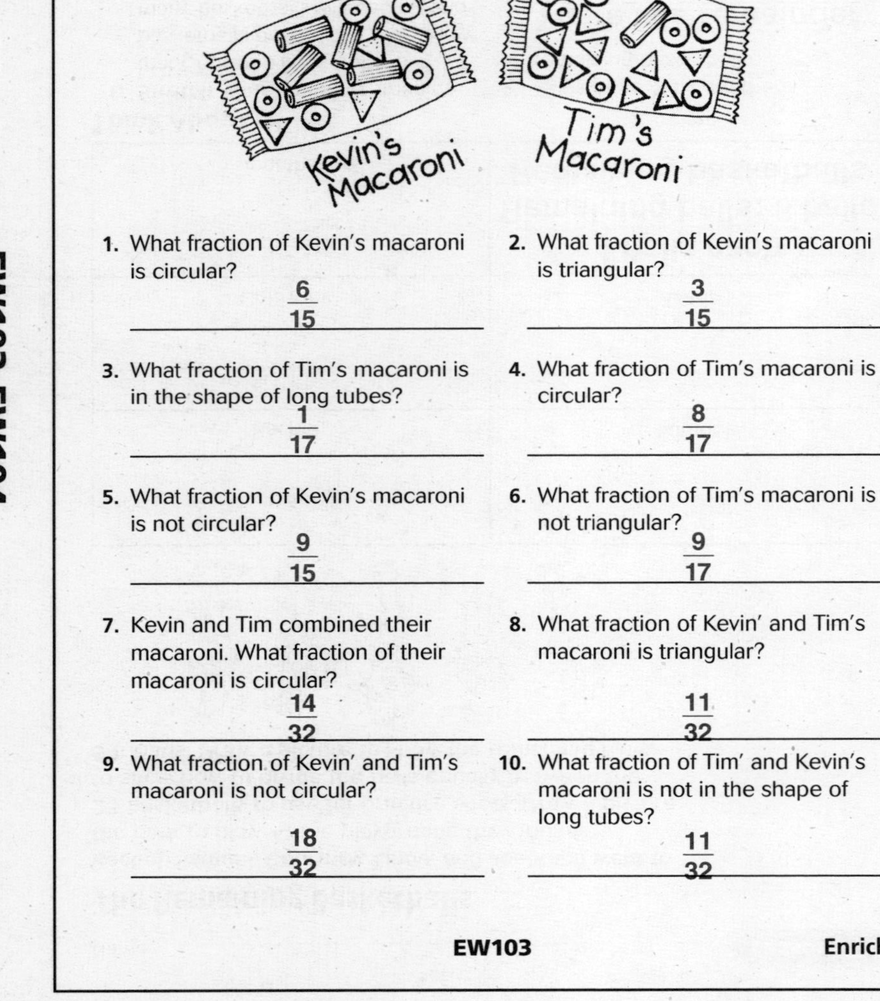

1. What fraction of Kevin's macaroni is circular? $\frac{6}{15}$
2. What fraction of Kevin's macaroni is triangular? $\frac{3}{15}$
3. What fraction of Tim's macaroni is in the shape of long tubes? $\frac{1}{17}$
4. What fraction of Tim's macaroni is circular? $\frac{8}{17}$
5. What fraction of Kevin's macaroni is not circular? $\frac{9}{15}$
6. What fraction of Tim's macaroni is not triangular? $\frac{9}{17}$
7. Kevin and Tim combined their macaroni. What fraction of their macaroni is circular? $\frac{14}{32}$
8. What fraction of Kevin' and Tim's macaroni is triangular? $\frac{11}{32}$
9. What fraction of Kevin' and Tim's macaroni is not circular? $\frac{18}{32}$
10. What fraction of Tim' and Kevin's macaroni is not in the shape of long tubes? $\frac{11}{32}$

Name____________________

Color the Equivalent Fractions

Color the picture below by finding fractions that are equivalent to the fractions shown in the key. You may use models to help you identify equivalent fractions.

$\frac{1}{2}$ = green $\frac{1}{3}$ = yellow
$\frac{1}{5}$ = black $\frac{1}{4}$ = brown
$\frac{2}{3}$ = blue 1 = orange

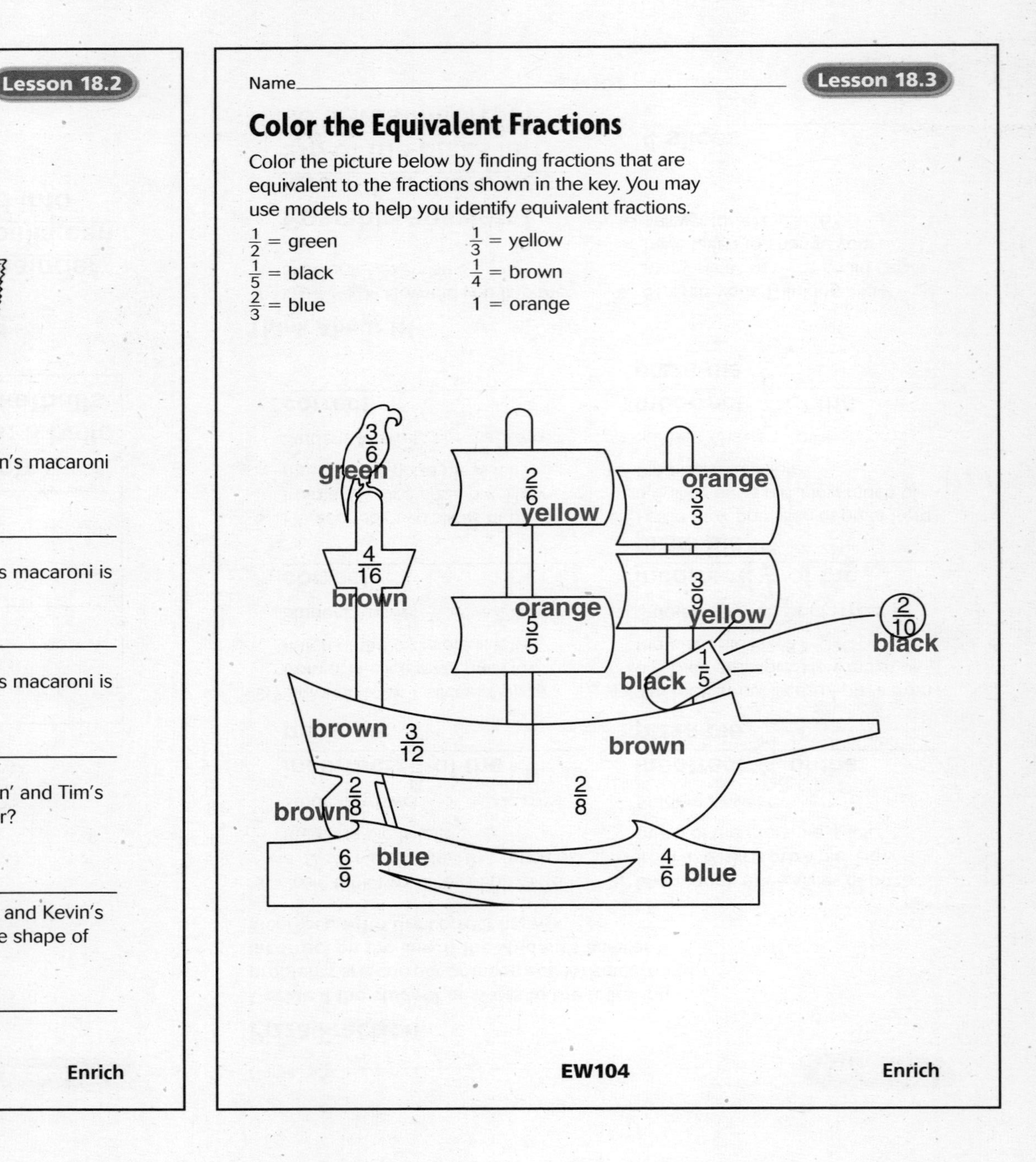

Name____________________ Lesson 18.4

What Fraction Am I?

Use the clues to find each fraction.

1. I am greater than $\frac{1}{5}$ and less than $\frac{1}{2}$. My denominator is between 2 and 4. What fraction am I?
   $\frac{1}{3}$

2. I am greater than $\frac{2}{8}$ and less than $\frac{4}{6}$. My denominator is 2. What fraction am I?
   $\frac{1}{2}$

3. I am equivalent to $\frac{1}{2}$. My numerator is 2. What fraction am I?
   $\frac{2}{4}$

4. I am less than $\frac{2}{6}$. My denominator is 3 times 2. What fraction am I?
   $\frac{1}{6}$

5. My denominator and my numerator can be divided by 5. I am equivalent to $\frac{1}{2}$. What fraction am I?
   $\frac{5}{10}$

6. I am a fraction equivalent to $\frac{6}{8}$. My denominator is 2×2. What fraction am I?
   $\frac{3}{4}$

7. I am greater than $\frac{5}{8}$ and less than 1. My numerator is 5. What fraction am I?
   $\frac{5}{6}$ or $\frac{5}{7}$

8. I am a fraction with a numerator of 3. My denominator is 4 times my numerator. What fraction am I?
   $\frac{3}{12}$

Think About It!

9. **Stretch Your Thinking** If exercise 8 had stated that "My denominator is 3 times my numerator," then what would the answer be? What is an eqivalent fraction for this answer?
   $\frac{3}{9}$; $\frac{2}{3}$

Name____________________ Lesson 18.5

Model Marbles

William has 12 marbles in a bag. Of these, $\frac{1}{6}$ are blue, $\frac{1}{2}$ are green, and $\frac{1}{3}$ are red.

Use this information to answer the questions below.

1. How can you use a number line, fraction bars, or fraction circles to make a model of this problem? Show your answer.
   show fraction bars for $\frac{1}{3}, \frac{1}{6}, \frac{1}{2}$; show a number line for $\frac{1}{3}, \frac{1}{2}, \frac{1}{6}$; show a pie with 6 pieces and 1 shaded, show a pie with 3 pieces and 1 shaded, show a pie with 2 pieces and 1 shaded

2. What color marbles does William have the least of? Use a model to show your work.
   blue

3. What color marbles does William have the most of? Use a model to show your work.
   green

4. If William combined his green and red marbles, then what would the sum be? Use model to show your work?
   10 marbles

5. If William combined his blue and red marbles, what would the sum be? Use a model to show your work?
   6 marbles

Name________________

Lesson 19.1

Let's Add Fractions

Fill in the gray squares to have correct addition across and down.

1.

$\frac{1}{4}$	+	$\frac{1}{4}$	=	$\frac{2}{4}$
+		+		+
$\frac{1}{4}$	+	$\frac{1}{4}$	=	$\frac{2}{4}$
=		=		=
$\frac{2}{4}$	+	$\frac{2}{4}$	=	1 or $\frac{4}{4}$

2.

$\frac{1}{6}$	+	$\frac{2}{6}$	=	$\frac{3}{6}$
+		+		+
$\frac{1}{6}$	+	$\frac{1}{6}$	=	$\frac{2}{6}$
=		=		=
$\frac{2}{6}$	+	$\frac{3}{6}$	=	$\frac{5}{6}$

3.

$\frac{2}{10}$	+	$\frac{4}{10}$	=	$\frac{6}{10}$
+		+		+
$\frac{2}{10}$	+	$\frac{1}{10}$	=	$\frac{3}{10}$
=		=		=
$\frac{4}{10}$	+	$\frac{5}{10}$	=	$\frac{9}{10}$

4.

$\frac{3}{12}$	+	$\frac{4}{12}$	=	$\frac{7}{12}$
+		+		+
$\frac{0}{12}$	+	$\frac{4}{12}$	=	$\frac{4}{12}$
=		=		=
$\frac{3}{12}$	+	$\frac{8}{12}$	=	$\frac{11}{12}$

Think About It!

1. WRITE Math How did you find the bottom right corner square for exercise 4?

Possible Answer: I added the top row and then added the sum to $\frac{4}{12}$

2. **Stretch Your Thinking** Finish the fraction squares for eighths below.

$\frac{1}{8}$	+	$\frac{1}{8}$	=	$\frac{2}{8}$
+		+		+
$\frac{3}{8}$	+	$\frac{3}{8}$	=	$\frac{6}{8}$
=		=		=
$\frac{4}{8}$	+	$\frac{4}{8}$	=	1

Name________________

Lesson 19.2

Fraction Recipes

Sara is writing a recipe book. If there are two ingredients that are similar Sara writes down the sum of these ingredients to help the people following her recipe book check their totals. For each problem below, write *"tasty"* on the line if Sara added her like fractions correctly and *"yuck"* on the line if Sara made an error in adding her fractions. If you write yuck then also write the correct sum.

1. For a cookie recipe Sara wrote down $\frac{1}{6}$ cup of grain sugar added with $\frac{1}{6}$ cup of brown sugar equals a total of $\frac{5}{6}$ cup of sugar.

   yuck $\frac{2}{6}$

2. For a casserole recipe Sara wrote down $\frac{1}{8}$ cup of paprika added with $\frac{3}{8}$ cup of parsley equals a total of $\frac{4}{8}$ cup of herbs.

   tasty

3. For a muffin recipe Sara wrote down $\frac{2}{10}$ cup of blueberries added with $\frac{5}{10}$ cup of blackberries equals a total of $\frac{6}{10}$ cup of fruits.

   yuck $\frac{7}{10}$

4. For a pizza recipe Sara wrote down $\frac{3}{4}$ cup of garlic added with $\frac{1}{4}$ cup of pepper equals a total of $\frac{5}{4}$ cup of spices.

   yuck 1 or $\frac{4}{4}$

5. For a pie recipe Sara wrote down $\frac{5}{12}$ cup of walnuts added with $\frac{5}{12}$ cup of pecans equals a total of $\frac{10}{12}$ cup of nuts.

   tasty

6. For a cake recipe Sara wrote down $\frac{1}{5}$ cup of grain sugar added to $\frac{4}{5}$ cup of brown sugar equals a total of 1 cup of sugar.

   tasty

Name________________ **Lesson 19.3**

Fraction Subtraction Pattern

Use fraction bars to show the next fraction in each pattern. Write the rule.

Example: $\frac{9}{9}$, $\frac{7}{9}$, $\frac{5}{9}$, $\frac{3}{9}$ Rule: Subtract $\frac{2}{9}$

1. $\frac{10}{10}$ $\frac{7}{10}$ $\frac{4}{10}$ ___

Rule: **$\frac{1}{10}$ subtract $\frac{3}{10}$**

2. $\frac{9}{9}$ $\frac{8}{9}$ $\frac{7}{9}$ ___

Rule: **$\frac{6}{9}$; subtract $\frac{1}{9}$**

3. $\frac{12}{12}$ $\frac{9}{12}$ $\frac{6}{12}$ ___

Rule: **$\frac{3}{12}$ or $\frac{1}{4}$; subtract $\frac{3}{12}$**

4. $\frac{8}{8}$ $\frac{6}{8}$ $\frac{4}{8}$ ___

Rule: **$\frac{2}{8}$ or $\frac{1}{4}$; subtract $\frac{2}{8}$**

5. $\frac{3}{4}$ $\frac{2}{4}$ $\frac{1}{4}$ ___

Rule: **0 subtract $\frac{1}{4}$**

6. $\frac{12}{12}$ $\frac{10}{12}$ $\frac{8}{12}$ ___

Rule: **$\frac{6}{12}$ or $\frac{1}{2}$; subtract $\frac{2}{12}$**

Think About It!

1. WRITE Math How did you know whether to subtract or add for each problem?

Possible Answer: The fractions kept getting smaller so I knew to subtract.

Name________________ 

Color by Differences

Color the following picture using the information in the box below.

$\frac{4}{5} - \frac{1}{5}$ = blue	$\frac{6}{8} - \frac{2}{8}$ = black	$\frac{12}{12} - \frac{5}{12}$ = yellow
$\frac{12}{12} - \frac{8}{12}$ = brown	$\frac{4}{4} - \frac{1}{4}$ = green	$\frac{3}{3} - \frac{1}{3}$ = gray

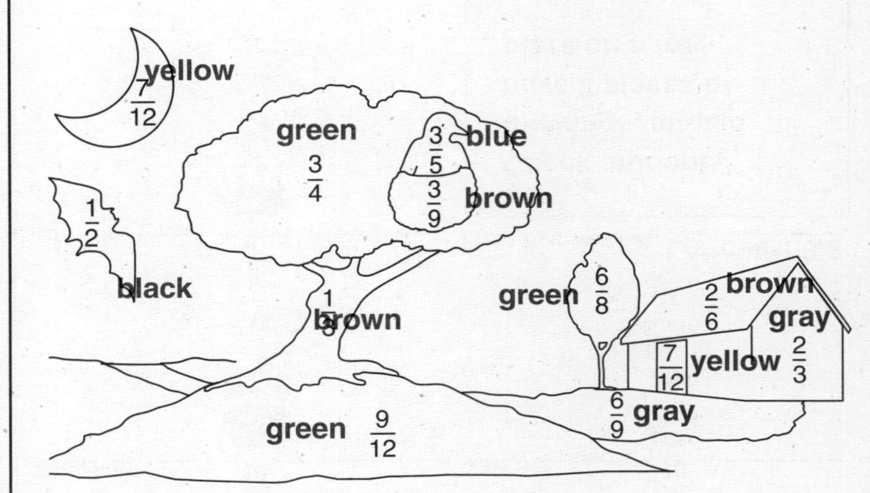

Missing Information

Can you figure out what's missing? Add the missing pieces of information. Then solve.

Answers will vary.

1. Gretta bought oranges, grapes, and pineapple to make a fruit salad. She bought $\frac{1}{8}$ pound of oranges and $\frac{3}{8}$ pound of grapes. How much fruit did Gretta buy altogether?

   Possible Answer: Gretta also bought $\frac{2}{8}$ pound of pineapple; $\frac{6}{8}$ or $\frac{3}{4}$ pound of fruit.

2. Deb is making 4 model bridges out of popsicle sticks. For her first bridge she used 20 sticks, for her second 15 sticks, and for her third 10 sticks. How many popsicle sticks did Deb use in all?

   Possible Answer: For her fourth bridge Deb used 19 sticks. 64 popsicle sticks

3. Mrs. Davis lost 3 items while traveling. She lost a comb and a toothbrush. If the airline wants a list in alphabetical order of her lost items. What will this list be?

   Possible Answer: Mrs. Davis also lost a shoe; comb, shoe, toothbrush

4. Charlie has traded in his tickets for 2 bouncing balls and 2 frisbees. How many tickets did it take to purchase each frisbee?

   Possible Answer: Each bouncing ball took 5 tickets to purchase; 15 tickets

Think About It!

5. WRITE Math How did you find the missing information for exercise 1?

   Possible Answer: I knew from the first sentence that she also bought pineapple.

Perfect Pizza Parts

David, Maria, and Rachel went to Perfect Pizza. They ordered a pizza with ten slices. Look at each picture and write a fraction to show what part of the pizza each person ate. Then draw a picture and write a decimal to show what part of the pizza was not eaten.

Rachel: $\frac{3}{10}$

David: $\frac{2}{10}$

Maria: $\frac{3}{10}$

Pizza that was left: **Leftover: 0.2**

Check students' drawings, should have 2 pieces of pizza on a tray.

Think About It!

1. WRITE Math Write decimals to show what part of the pizza Rachel, Maria, and David each ate.

   0.3, 0.3, 0.2

   Check for accuracy.

2. WRITE Math Explain how you determined the part of the pizza that was not eaten.

   Answers will vary.

   Check students' explanations.

Name__________

Match the Model

1–6. Answers shown.

Draw lines to match the hundredths decimal model on the left with the fraction in the middle. Then draw lines to match each fraction in the middle with the decimal on the right.

1. $\frac{6}{100}$ 0.17
2. $\frac{30}{100}$ 0.42
3. $\frac{2}{100}$ 0.06
4. $\frac{21}{100}$ 0.02
5. $\frac{42}{100}$ 0.30
6. $\frac{17}{100}$ 0.21

Think About It!

7. WRITE Math Explain how you found the decimal for $\frac{2}{100}$.

Possible Answer: I looked for a decimal with a 0 in the tenths place and a 2 in the hundredths place.

8. Use a place value chart to write the sum, 0.3 + 0.09.

Check students' work; should be 0 in the ones place, 3 in the tenths place, and 9 in the hundredths place.

Name__________

Be Careful of Those Greater Than One

Circle the errors in each problem. Write the correct answer for each.

1.

Ones		Tenths	Hundredths
8	.	2	4

eight and twenty-four tenths
8 + 0.2 + 0.04

eight and twenty-four tenths should be eight and twenty-four hundredths

2.

Ones		Tenths	Hundredths
2	.	0	3

two and three hundredths
2 + (0.3)

2 + 0.3 should be 2 + 0.03

3.

Ones		Tenths	Hundredths
3	.	2	1

(thirty-two and one hundredth)
3 + 0.2 + 0.01

thirty-two and one hundredth should be three and twenty-one hundredths

4.

Ones		Tenths	Hundredths
7	.	1	0

seven and one tenth
7 + (0.01)

7 + 0.01 should be 7 + 0.1

Think About It!

5. WRITE Math How did you find the error for exercise 4?

I realized 1 hundredth was being added when the table shows that 1 tenth should be added

6. **Stretch Your Thinking** If two and one tenth were added to three and ninety-four hundreths, would the sum be greater than 6?

Yes

Name______________________ Lesson 20.4

Money Match

Draw lines to match the coins on the left to the money amount in the middle. Then draw lines from the money amount in the middle to the correct fraction on the right.

Coins	Amount	Fraction
1. 1 quarter, 3 dimes, 6 pennies	$0.96	$\frac{61}{100}$
2. 2 quarters, 1 dime, 5 pennies	$0.23	$\frac{96}{100}$
3. 3 quarters, 2 dimes, 1 penny	$0.61	$\frac{55}{100}$
4. 6 dimes, 3 nickels, 2 pennies	$0.55	$\frac{23}{100}$
5. 4 nickels, 3 pennies	$0.65	$\frac{77}{100}$
6. 1 quarter, 2 dimes, 1 nickel, 5 pennies	$0.77	$\frac{65}{100}$

Think About It!

7. WRITE Math How did you find the answer for exercise 5?

I multiplied $0.05 times 4 and $0.01 times three then added the products

8. **Stretch Your Thinking** If a person had $\frac{61}{100}$ of a dollar in their left pocket, then gained an additional $0.45, then lost a one-dollar bill, could they still have $1.06? Explain.

Yes; they might have had a one-dollar bill in a different pocket to start

Name______________________ Lesson 20.5

What's Missing?

Write the missing number for each problem.

1. 0.■ **8** − 0.1 = 0.7

2. 0.4 + 0.■ **8** = 1.2

3. 0.■ **9** − 0.7 = 0.2

4. 7.9■ **1** − 5.81 = 2.10

5. 5.37 + 2.6■ **3** = 8.00

6. 4.■3 **7** − 3.82 = 0.91

7. $7.8■ **3** − $2.68 = $5.15

8. $1.77 + $8.■4 **3** = $10.11

9. $7.■3 **8** − $0.84 = $6.99

10. 4.6 + 3.■ **8** + 1.5 = 9.9

11. ■.1 **8** + 7.4 + 1.6 = 17.1

12. 5.5 + 2.5 + 3.■ **6** = 11.6

Think About It!

13. What is an easy way to get the wrong answer while adding money amounts, even though the correct numbers and decimal placement is written in the answer?

not bringing down the dollar sign

14. WRITE Math How did you find the missing number for exercise 9?

I added $0.84 with $6.99

Name____________________ Lesson 20.6

Make a Model

Shade the necessary amount of decimal squares to represent each money amount. If you know that over $\frac{1}{2}$ of the decimal squares for an exercise will be shaded use blue to shade. If you know that over $\frac{1}{4}$, but less than $\frac{1}{2}$, of the decimal squares for an exercise will be shaded then use green to shade. For all other amounts, use gray to shade.

Check number of squares shaded 1–5

1. $0.57

2. $0.29

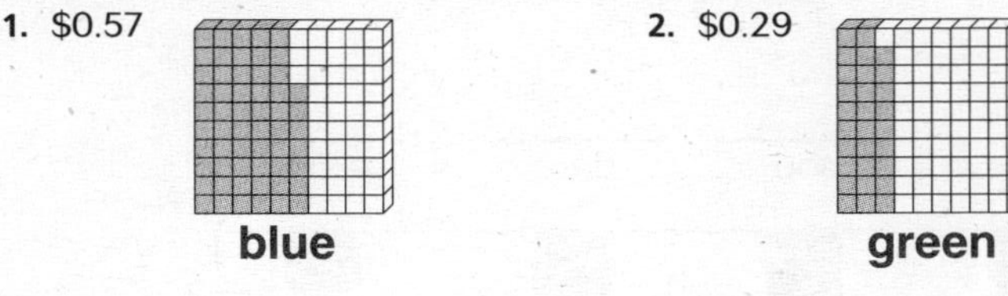

blue　　green

3. $0.49

4. $0.10

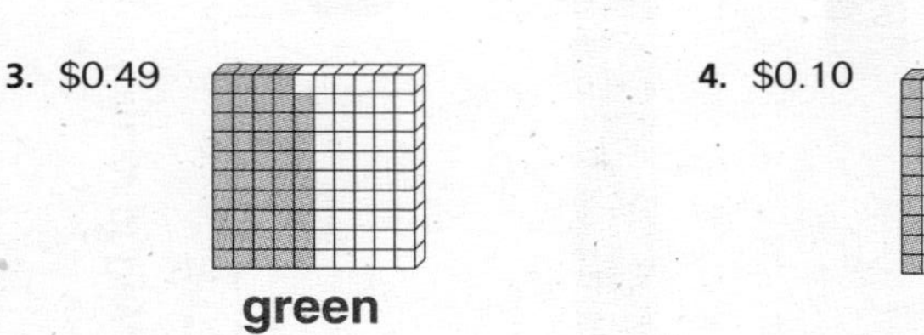

green　　gray

5. $2.02

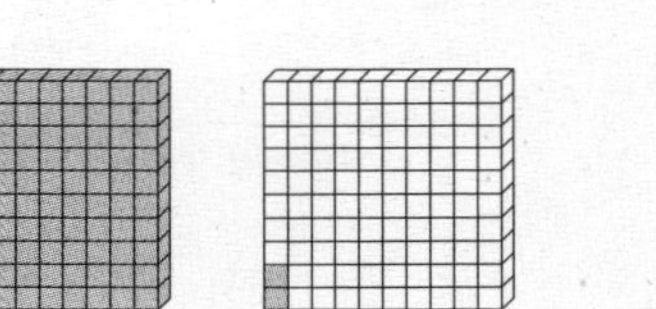

blue

Think About It!

6. If a decimal square model is completely shaded, what does this represent?

the whole number 1

Name____________________ Lesson 21.1

The Experiment Gone Tally

Make number cards numbered 1-5. Mix up the cards and place them face down. Choose a card. Mark a tally in the tally table below next to the number on the card you choose. Return the card to the pile. Repeat this 15 times.

Number Experiment	
Number	**Tallies**
1	
2	
3	
4	
5	

1. What number card did you choose most often? __________

2. Did you select more cards numbered 1 and 2 or more cards numbered 3 and 4? __________

3. How many more cards numbered 5 did you select than cards with 1? _____

Answers will vary.

Think About It!

4. WRITE Math If the cards were numbered 1, 1, 2, 3, 4, instead of 1, 2, 3, 4, 5, how might your tally table change? Explain.

Possible answer: the table would have more tallies beside the Number 1 and no tallies beside the Number 5.

Name ______________________ Lesson 21.2

Food Bar

Create and label a bar graph to group the data in the following scenario. Color each of the bars you create a different color.

Chuck ate only tacos, salad, soup, and rice during the month of June. He ate tacos 2 out of 30 days, salad 10 out of 30 days, soup 14 out of 30 days, and rice 4 out of 30 days.

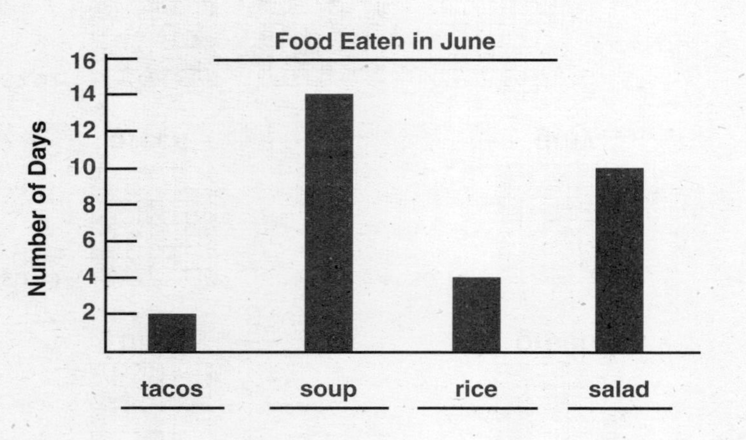

Think About It!

1. WRITE Math How do you know what to label the scale?
   Possible answer: I knew I had to label the scale by 2s because there are only 8 marks and Chuck ate tacos 14 days.

2. **Stretch Your Thinking** What if Chuck had eaten tacos 0 days? How would your bar for tacos have changed?
   the bar for tacos would not be present

Name ______________________ Lesson 21.3

Pick the Golden Duck

Mr. Mitchell's class runs a game at the school carnival called "Pick the Golden Duck." People who play the game must put on a blindfold and then pick one duck out of the pond. The ducks are all of equal size.

green fewer likely orange unlikely fewer certain golden

Carefully read each statement below.

- There is only 1 Golden Duck.
- Picking a blue duck is more likely than picking the Golden Duck.
- Picking a red duck is more likely than picking a blue duck.
- Picking a green duck is more likely than picking a red duck.

Possible Answer for colors:
1 golden
2 blue
3 red
7 green

Use the words from the pond to fill in the blanks below. Each word may be used only once. Cross out each word as you use it. Then color in the ducks to make your answers true.

1. There are more **green** ducks in the pond than any other color.
2. There are **fewer** red ducks in the pond than green ducks.
3. There are **fewer** blue ducks in the pond than red ducks.
4. There are more blue ducks in the pond than **golden** ducks.
5. Picking the Golden Duck is **unlikely** but not impossible.
6. Picking an **orange** duck is impossible.
7. Picking a green duck is **likely**.
8. Picking a duck with color is **certain**.

Name________________

Uncertain Outcomes

Jenna, Scott, and Rebecca are bobbing for apples. They have asked you to help them. In the apple tub below, color 4 apples red, 3 apples green, and 1 apple yellow.

Before bobbing for apples, Jenna, Scott, and Rebecca make predictions. Jenna is going to bob first, Scott second, and Rebecca third. Write whether their predictions are *correct* or *incorrect*.

1. Jenna's prediction: "I will most likely pick a yellow apple."
   incorrect
2. Scott's prediction: "If Jenna picks a red apple, I will most likely pick either a red apple or a green apple."
   correct
3. Rebecca's prediction: "If both Jenna and Scott pick red apples, I will most likely pick a green apple."
   correct

After bobbing for apples, Jenna, Scott, and Rebecca tell which apple they have picked. Write whether these outcomes are *unlikely, likely,* or *equally likely*.

4. Jenna: "I went first. I picked a red apple."
   likely
5. Scott: "I went second. I picked a yellow apple."
   unlikely
6. Rebecca: "I went third. I picked a red apple."
   equally likely

Think About It!

7. **Stretch Your Thinking** What are the possible outcomes if Jenna takes another turn after Rebecca? **red, green**

Name________________

Experiment Mix-Up

Oh no! A gust of wind has mixed up the probability experiments in Mrs. Nelson's class. The students wrote their names on their tally tables but not on their spinners or results. In Column B, write the name of the student whose tally table matches the spinner. In Column C, write the names of all the students who might get the result shown. Each spinner's sections are of equal size.

Column A: Tally Tables

Tate's Experiment

Color	Tally
Stripes	IIII
Polka Dots	IIII
Gray	卌 I
Black	III
White	III

Natalie's Experiment

Color	Tally
White	IIII
Polka Dots	III
Gray	卌
Black	卌 III

Megan's Experiment

Color	Tally
Gray	卌 卌
Black	IIII
White	卌 I

Column B: Spinners

1. **Tate**
2. **Megan**
3. **Natalie**

Column C: Results

4. Black and White are equally likely outcomes.
   Tate
   Megan
   Natalie
5. Polka Dots are an impossible outcome.
   Megan
6. Stripes are an impossible outcome.
   Megan
   Natalie

Name ______________________ Lesson 21.6

Line Plot Rating

Hank interpreted the line plot below. The line plot documents the heights of a group of football players. Decide whether Hank's interpretations are correct or incorrect.

4	5	6	7
X	XXXXX	XXXX	XXX

Height of Football Players (in ft.)

1. Hank said, "The mode of this data is 7."
   Is Hank correct or incorrect?
   incorrect

2. Hank said, "The range of this data is 2."
   Is Hank correct or incorrect?
   incorrect

3. Hank said, "The information about the height of the football players is arranged in a pictograph on this page."
   Is Hank correct or incorrect?
   incorrect

4. Hank said, "There are more 5 ft tall players than there are 6 ft tall players, according to this data."
   Is Hank correct or incorrect?
   correct

Think About It!

5. WRITE Math How did you find the answer for exercise 2?
   I subtracted the least number in the set of data from the greatest number. The difference is 3 so Hank's answer is incorrect.

6. **Stretch Your Thinking** What if there had been no 7 ft tall players? How would this affect the answer to exercise 2?
   the answer would change from incorrect to correct

Name ______________________ Lesson 21.7

Lightning Strike Predictions

Amidst a very rainy season Dr. Plume, a meteorologist, took some scientific observations about lightning strikes during a 5 day period.

Dr. Plume's Observations

Day	Number of Lightning Strikes
Monday	20
Tuesday	16
Wednesday	21
Thursday	16
Friday	20

Write whether the people who are now making predictions, based upon Dr. Plume's findings, are correct or incorrect about what will probably happen on the Saturday following the fifth day of Dr. Plume's experiment.

1. Mrs. Stroud says it is likely that lightning will strike 21 times on Saturday.
   incorrect

2. Mr. Burns says that it is more likely that lightning will strike 20 times on Saturday rather than 21 times.
   correct

3. Ms. Lucas says that on Saturday it is equally likely that lightning will strike 21 times or 16 times.
   incorrect

4. Dr. Plume predicts that lightning will strike either 16 times or 20 times on Saturday.
   correct

Think About It!

5. WRITE Math What if Dr. Plume had recorded 8 lightning strikes on Thursday? How would this affect the answer for exercise 4?
   The answer would change from correct to incorrect

EW125-EW126

Name________________ Lesson 21.8

Picky Eaters

Use the information below to make an organized list for each question. Then solve.

Mary invites 7 friends over to watch a movie. Each friend brings either a snack or a drink to share. Gary brings grapes. Ben brings bananas. Paul brings pears. Anton brings apples. Wendy brings water. Lily brings lemonade. Alice brings apple juice. Ben says, "I eat only grapes." Anton says, "I don't drink lemonade."

1. How many possible 1 snack and 1 drink combinations are there in all? 12

grapes — **water**, **lemonade**, **apple juice**
bananas — **water**, **lemonade**, **apple juice**
pears — **water**, **lemonade**, **apple juice**
apples — **water**, **lemonade**, **apple juice**

2. How many possible 1 snack and 1 drink combinations can Ben have? 3

grapes — **water**, **lemonade**, **apple juice**

3. How many possible 1 snack and 1 drink combinations can Anton have? 8

grapes — **water**, **apple juice**
bananas — **water**, **apple juice**
pears — **water**, **apple juice**
apples — **water**, **apple juice**

Name________________ Lesson 22.1

Money Monster!

The Money Monster eats only money! On Mondays, Wednesdays, and Fridays the Money Monster eats only amounts greater than $5.00. On Tuesdays and Thursdays, he eats only amounts less than $5.00. On Saturdays and Sundays, he eats only amounts equal to $5.00.

Look at the money amounts below. Then write each exercise number of the money amount under the correct day, for which the Money Monster will eat that amount, at the bottom of the page.

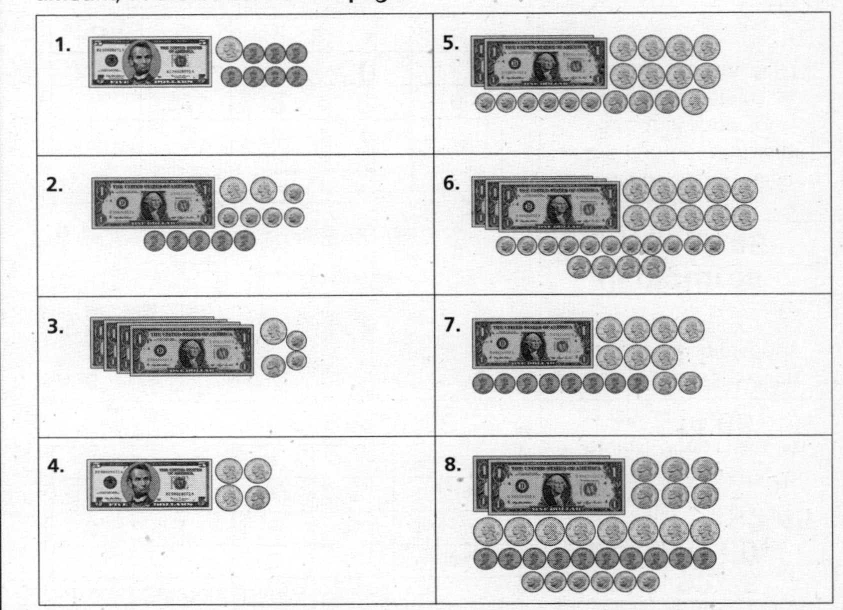

Monday, Wednesday, and Friday	Tuesday and Thursday	Saturday and Sunday
1, 4, 6	2, 3, 7	5, 8

Name

Is This the Correct Change?

The buyers in the problems below bought the items directly to the right of their respective problems. Read each problem. If the change is correct, write *correct*. If the change is incorrect, write *incorrect*. Then write the correct amount of change.

1. Mae pays with a $5 bill. Mae receives $1.00 in change.
   incorrect; $1.75

2. Warren pays with a $10 bill. Warren receives $7.50 in change.
   correct

3. Tia pays with two $5 bills. Tia receives $3.10 in change.
   correct

4. Chris pays with two $10 bills. Chris receives $2.50 in change.
   incorrect; $5.75

5. Malcolm pays for his movie ticket with a $10 bill. Malcolm receives $2.75 in change.
   incorrect; $2.50

6. Hayley pays with one $10 bill, one $5 bill, three $1 bills, 2 quarters, and 3 dimes. Hayley receives $0.03 in change.
   incorrect; $0.04

Name

Money Strategies

Look at each table and picture. Then fill in the answers to the problems that use this information.

$1 Bills	Quarters	Dimes	Nickels	
5	4	2	1	Monday
3	1	5	0	Tuesday
0	5	1	5	Thursday
1	3	4	6	Friday

1. Lisa earns **$6.25** on Monday, **$3.75** on Tuesday, **$1.60** on Thursday, and **$2.45** on Friday. How much money does Lisa earn in all? **$14.05**

A
B
C
D

2. Sal has $1.45. Which picture of coins does Sal have?
   all pictures equal $1.45

$1 Bills	Quarters	Dimes	Nickels	Pennies
3	**3**	0	0	0
3	2	**2**	1	0
3	2	2	**0**	5
3	2	1	2	5

3. Mel has $3.75. Fill in the number of bills or coins that show four equivalent sets of money equaling $3.75.

Think About It!

4. **Stretch Your Thinking** Susie received 2 quarters, 6 dimes, and 7 nickels for helping her mom with the charts. When she checked her pocket again, she only had $1.30. What 2 coins did Susie lose?
   1 nickel and 1 dime

5. **Stretch your thinking** Keli has 4 quarters, 3 dimes and 2 nickels in her ceramic bank. Her uncle gave her 2 more coins. She now has $1.75. What 2 coins did Keli's uncle give her?
   1 quarter and 1 dime

Name________________ Lesson 22.4

What's Missing?

Uh-oh! Jeff dropped some of his play money while he was modeling some money addition problems. Look at the problems below to find the missing number. Then list the coin, coins, or bills Jeff needs to fill in the blanks. The first one is done for you.

1. $0.□9 + $0.11 = $0.70
   5; 2 quarters

2. $10.41 + $7.3□ = $17.72
   1; 1 penny

3. $10.□5 + $1.71 = $11.96
   2; 2 dimes

4. $7.9□ + $5.81 = $13.80
   9; 9 pennies

5. $5.37 + $2.6□ = $8.00
   3; 3 pennies

6. $4.□3 + $3.82 = $8.05
   2; 2 dimes

7. $7.8□ + $1.18 = $9.05
   7; 7 pennies

8. $1.77 + $8.□4 = $10.11
   3; 3 dimes

9. $7.□3 + $2.19 = $9.92
   7; 2 quarters, 2 dimes

10. $4.67 + $3.□3 + $1.55 = $9.35
    1; 1 dime

11. $□.21 + $7.40 + $1.63 = $17.24
    8; 8 $1 bills

12. $5.55 + $2.50 + $2.□5 = $10.60
    5; 2 quarters

Name________________ Lesson 22.5

Missing Money Values

Write the missing money value for each problem.

1. $0.□1 − $0.13 = $0.78
   $0.90

2. $20.41 − $7.3□ = $13.02
   $0.09

3. $10.□5 − $1.71 = $8.54
   $0.20

4. $7.9□ − $5.81 = $2.09
   $0.00

5. $5.37 − $2.6□ = $2.68
   $0.09

6. $3.□3 − $3.88 = $0.05
   $0.90

7. $7.8□ − $1.18 = $6.65
   $0.03

8. $9.13 − $8.□4 = $0.19
   $0.90

9. $7.□3 − $2.19 = $5.34
   $0.50

10. $4.67 − $3.□3 = $0.84
    $0.80

11. $□.21 − $5.40 = $1.81
    $7.00

12. $8.50 − $5.□5 = $2.95
    $0.50

Think About It!

13. **Stretch Your Thinking** Can you solve the missing money value problem below? If not, why not? If so, how?

$□.□□ − $2.69 = $6.83

Yes. I add the difference to the value shown and I get $9.52

Name______________________ Lesson 22.6

Shopping for a Money Match

Draw lines to match the description to the item or items purchased.

1. Allie buys 3 of the same item. She pays with two $10 bills. She receives $8.03 in change. Which item does Allie buy?

2. Erik buys 2 sports items. He spends $10.00. He doesn't receive any change. Which 2 items does he buy?

3. Ryan buys 4 items. He pays with two $10 bills. He receives $3.32 in change. Which 4 items does Ryan buy?

4. Betty and Linda buy 4 items in all. Together they spend $5.00. They buy 2 of one item and 2 of another. Which items do they buy?

5. Debbie bought 1 item. She paid with one $5 bill, three $1 bills, 6 quarters, and 5 dimes. She received $0.02 in change. Which item did Debbie buy?

6. Astra's mom gave her some colored paper and $3.00 to buy the other supplies for an art project. She received $0.31 in change. Which item did Astra buy?

7. Melissa is going to a party for the triplets Billy, Bobby, and Bradley.
   She wants to buy each boy a different item as a present. She has $20. First, she buys a party hat. What three other items can she buy as presents without going over $20?

$4.75 $3.99 $1.25 $5.25 $2.69 CRAYONS $9.98 $1.25

Dashed lines are possible answers.

Name______________________ Lesson 22.7

Time Match

Draw lines to match the clocks on the left with the time on the right.

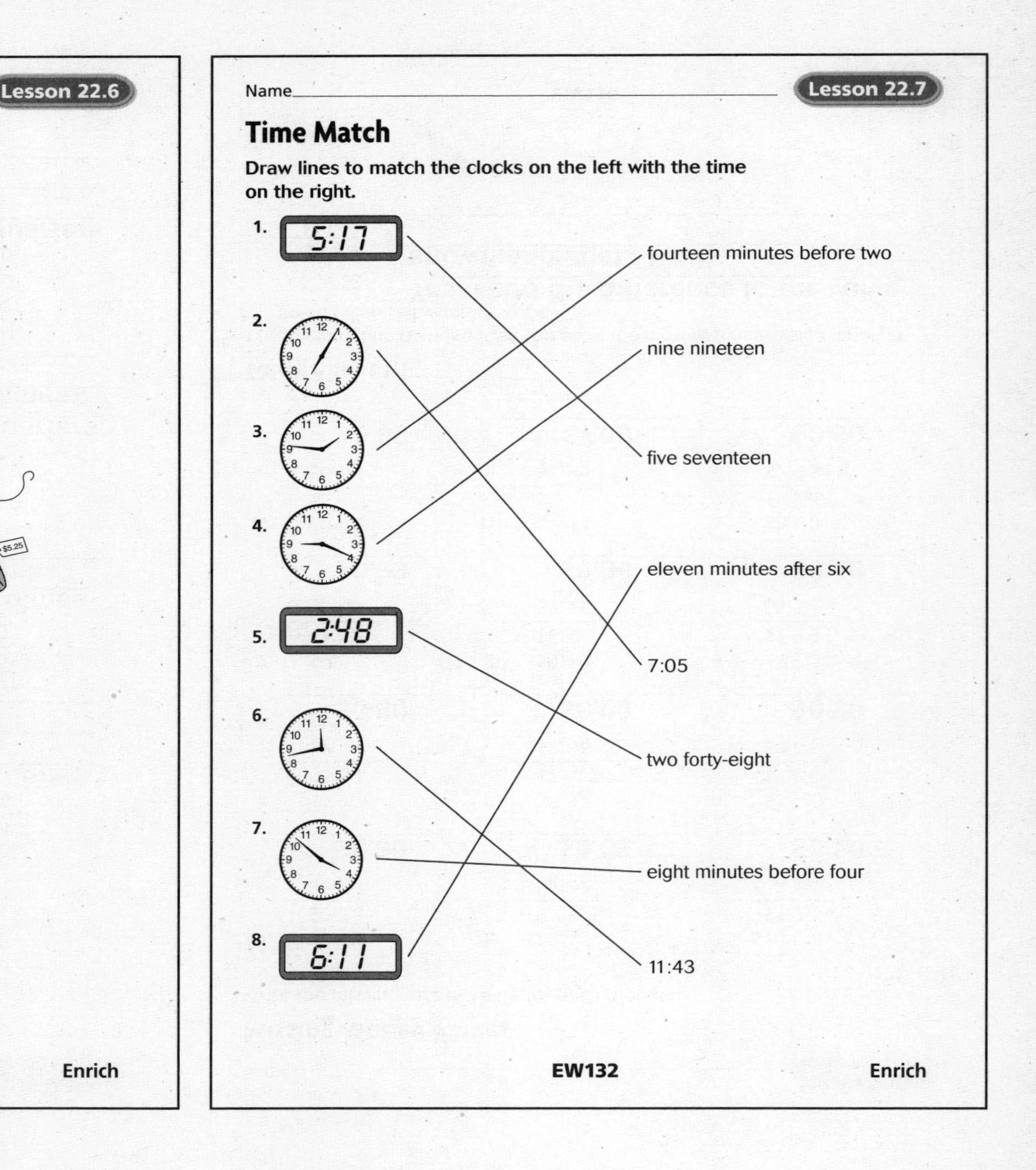

Name________________________

Time Order

A.M. stands for *ante meridiem*. *Ante meridiem* means "before the meridian" in Latin. P.M. stands for *post meridiem*. *Post meridiem* means "after the meridian" in Latin. The meridian is an imaginary line. It represents noon.

For the problems below, use A.M. or P.M. to write the time for each activity. Then, write the time of each activity in sequential order. Draw a meridian line where noon takes place in the sequential time.

1.

10:30 pm	8:14 a.m	6:00 pm	3:00 pm
dream	ride the bus to school	eat dinner	piano lesson
A.M. 8:24 a.m	3:00 pm	6:00 pm	P.M. 10:30 pm

2.

5:00 pm	1:15 pm	7:10 a.m	10:00 a.m
do home work	gym class	wake up	go to the library
A.M. 7:10 a.m	10:00 a.m	12:25 pm	P.M. 5:00 pm

Name________________________

Draw The Clocks

Read the pattern. Then, write the time using A.M. or P.M. Finally draw the hands on the clock to show your answer.

1. Jason left school at 4:15 in the afternoon. It is now 55 minutes later. What time is it?

   5:10 P.M.

2. Larry ate dinner at 5:20 in the afternoon. He is at the ball park now and it is 35 minutes later. What time is it?

   5:55 P.M.

3. Gail woke up at 6:45 in the morning. She is now at school and it is 40 minutes later. What time is it?

   7:25 A.M.

4. Jenny played in the yard at 7:40 in the evening. She is now in bed and it is 25 minutes later. What time is it?

   8:05 P.M.

5. Sam did his homework until 3:40 in the afternoon. Now he is riding his bike and it is 45 minutes later. What time is it?

   4:25 P.M.

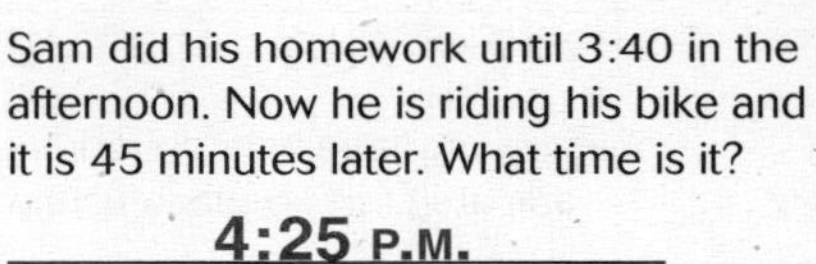

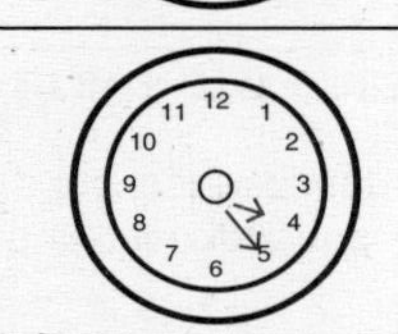

Think About It!

6. **Stretch Your Thinking** If exercise 2 had read: "Larry ate dinner at 5:20 in the afternoon. He is at the ball park now and it is fifteen hours and 35 minutes later. What time is it?" What would the new answer for exercise 2 be?

   8:55 A.M.

Name

Calendar Riddles

Read the calendar. Then solve the riddles.

July						
S	M	T	W	T	F	S
26	**27**	**28**	**29**	**30**	1	2
3	4	5	6	7	8	9
10	11	12	13	14	15	16
17	18	19	20	21	22	23
24	25	26	27	28	29	30
31	**1**	**2**	**3**	**4**	**5**	**6**

1. I am the third Friday in July. What is my date? **July 15**
2. I am the day after July 15. What day of the week am I? **July 16, Saturday**
3. I am July 23. What day of the week am I? **Saturday**
4. I am the Tuesday after July 6. What is my date? **July 12**
5. I am 1 week after July 7. What is my date? **July 14**
6. I am the last day of July. What day of the week am I? **July 31, Sunday**
7. I am the fifth day of July. What day of the week am I? **Tuesday**
8. I am the second to last day of July. What is my date? **July 30**

Think About It!

9. **Stretch Your Thinking** June comes before July. July comes Before August. Fill in the blank days on the calendar above with the correct dates for June and August.

See annos in page.

Name

Event Hunt

Use the time line to answer the questions.

1867	1871	1883	1908	1914	1915	1931
Alaska sold to U.S	Fire destroys Chicago	Brooklyn Bridge opens	first Ford cars made	Panama Canal opens	first telephone call	Empire State building opens

1. Which event on the time line happened first, after the Chicago fire? **Brooklyn Bridge opens**
2. Which event happened 7 years before the first telephone call? **the first Ford cars made**
3. How long after the Brooklyn Bridge opened did the Panama Canal open? **31 years**
4. Which event happened about 40 years after Alaska was sold to the United States? **the first Ford cars made**
5. Which happened first—the first Ford cars, or the first telephone call? **Ford cars**
6. Which happened later—the opening of the Empire State Building or the Panama Canal? **the Empire State building**
7. Where would you rather be in 1871—Chicago or Alaska? Why? **Alaska because there was a great fire in Chicago that year**
8. Which is the first event that happened in the 1900s? Which is the last event of the 1800s? **Ford cars; Brooklyn Bridge**

Name________________

Lesson 23.1

Unit Choice

Decide whether the unit chosen to measure the objects below is correct or incorrect.

1. Gus measured the length of the bowl of fruit below in miles.

Did Gus use the best unit to measure? Explain.

no; should have used inches or feet

2. Sandra measured the length of the pair of scissors below in yards.

Did Sandra use the best unit to measure? Explain.

no; should have used inches

3. Tommy measured the distance around the model of the globe below in yards.

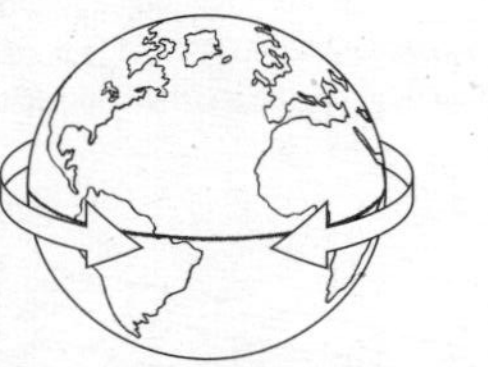

Did Tommy use the best unit to measure? Explain.

yes; feet would also work

4. Lisa measured the height of the flower below in miles.

Did Lisa use the best unit to measure? Explain.

no; should have used inches possible feet

Think About It!

5. WRITE Math Explain how you found the answer for exercise 4.

no flowers measure a mile

Name________________

Lesson 23.2

Farmhouse Inches

Use an inch ruler to measure each line on the pictures of the farmhouse objects below. For each exercise write an exact measurement, an estimate to the nearest inch, and an estimate to the nearest half-inch.

EXACT; $5\frac{1}{2}$ inches
NEAREST INCH; 6 inches
1. **NEAREST HALF—INCH $5\frac{1}{2}$ inches**

EXACT; $2\frac{5}{6}$ inches
NEAREST INCH; 3 inches
2. **NEAREST HALF—INCH 3 inches**

EXACT; $1\frac{3}{8}$ inches
NEAREST INCH; 1 inch
NEAREST HALF–INCH
3. **$1\frac{1}{2}$ inches**

Think About It!

4. WRITE Math How did you find the estimated answer for exercise 3?

I measured the line, it measured $1\frac{3}{8}$ inches, which to the nearest inch is 1 inch rounded down, and to the nearest half-inch is $1\frac{1}{2}$ inches rounded up.

Name________________ Lesson 23.3

Watch Your Feet!

Decide whether the estimates for the objects below are reasonable. The actual measurements are given.

1. Sue's Estimate: 30 feet

Actual Measurement: 24 feet
Is Sue's Estimate reasonable?
Explain.
No, a more reasonable estimate would be 20 feet since 24 is closer to 20 than to 30.

2. Lane's Estimate: 108 inches

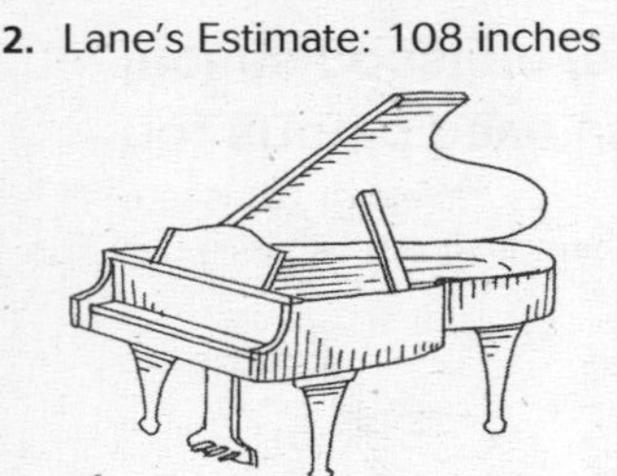

Actual Measurement: 3 yards
Is Lane's Estimate reasonable?
Explain.
Yes, a yard equals 3 feet and a foot equals 12 inches, so 3 yards equals 108 inches

3. Victor's Estimate: 20 yards

Actual Measurement: 19 miles
Is Victor's Estimate reasonable?
Explain.
No, 20 yards is not even close to 19 miles. The more reasonable estimate would have read 20 miles.

4. Paula's Estimate: 20 inches

Actual Measurement: 18 inches
Is Paula's Estimate reasonable?
Explain.
Yes, 18 inches can be estimated at 20 inches.

Name________________ Lesson 23.4

Capacity Riddle

Circle the best estimate of the capacity for each item. Write the letter of your answer in the blank at the bottom of the page.

1. a mug
   - (M) 1 cup
   - N 1 quart
2. a kitchen sink
   - O 5 quarts
   - (E) 5 gallons
3. a fish tank
   - (A) 10 gallons
   - E 10 cups
4. a pool
   - (S) 1,000 gallons
   - T 1,000 cups
5. a thermos
   - E 10 quarts
   - (U) 10 cups
6. a bowl of soup
   - (R) 1 pint
   - H 1 gallon
7. a carton of milk
   - I 1 cup
   - (E) 1 quart
8. a bottle of water
   - D 2 gallons
   - (C) 2 pints
9. a juice box
   - (A) 1 cup
   - B 1 gallon
10. a bathtub
    - K 40 cups
    - (P) 40 gallons
11. a small fish bowl
    - C 4 gallons
    - (A) 4 quarts
12. a pot of coffee
    - (C) 8 cups
    - T 8 gallons
13. a mixing bowl
    - O 1 cup
    - (I) 1 gallon
14. a dog's bowl
    - J 1 gallon
    - (T) 1 pint
15. a tea kettle
    - E 3 gallons
    - (Y) 3 quarts

What do cups, pints, quarts, and gallons do?

M	E	A	S	U	R	E		C	A	P	A	C	I	T	Y
1	2	3	4	5	6	7		8	9	10	11	12	13	14	15

Name____________________

From Lightest to Heaviest

Write each series of objects in order from the lightest weight to the heaviest weight.

1. book, piece of paper, desk

   piece of paper, book, desk

2. orange, grape, watermelon

   grape, orange, watermelon

3. flower, tree, leaf

   leaf, flower, tree

4. tennis player, tennis ball, tennis racket

   tennis ball, tennis racket, tennis player

5. baseball, baseball player, baseball bat

   baseball, baseball bat, baseball player

6. cereal bowl, spoon, napkin

   napkin, spoon, cereal bowl

7. chicken, goldfish, cow

   goldfish, chicken, cow

Think About It!

8. WRITE Math Explain how you decided the order of the items in the exercises.

   Possible answer: I first found the lightest object and wrote it down. I then found the heaviest object and wrote it down leaving space in the middle of these two objects to write the name of the third object not yet identified.

Name____________________

Estimate or Measure

Choose estimate or measure for each situation. Then unscramble the letters in front of each answer to solve the riddle below.

1. Eve kicked a ball across the playground. Did Eve estimate or measure, the distance the ball traveled?

   (Y) Estimate
   T Measure

2. Ellie made lasagna. She added 3 cups of diced tomatoes. Did Ellie estimate or measure, the amount of tomatoes?

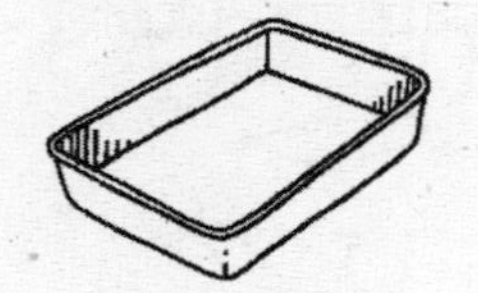

   E Estimate
   (A) Measure

3. Ivy filled her dog's bowl with water each morning. Did Ivy estimate or measure, the amount of water?

   (R) Estimate
   Z Measure

4. Lincoln made an 8-foot-wide wooden deck. Did Lincoln estimate or measure, the length of the wooden boards?

   T Estimate
   (D) Measure

Riddle: **I can be part of a house or a school. I can be measured by feet. What am I?**

Answer: **Y** **A** **R** **D**

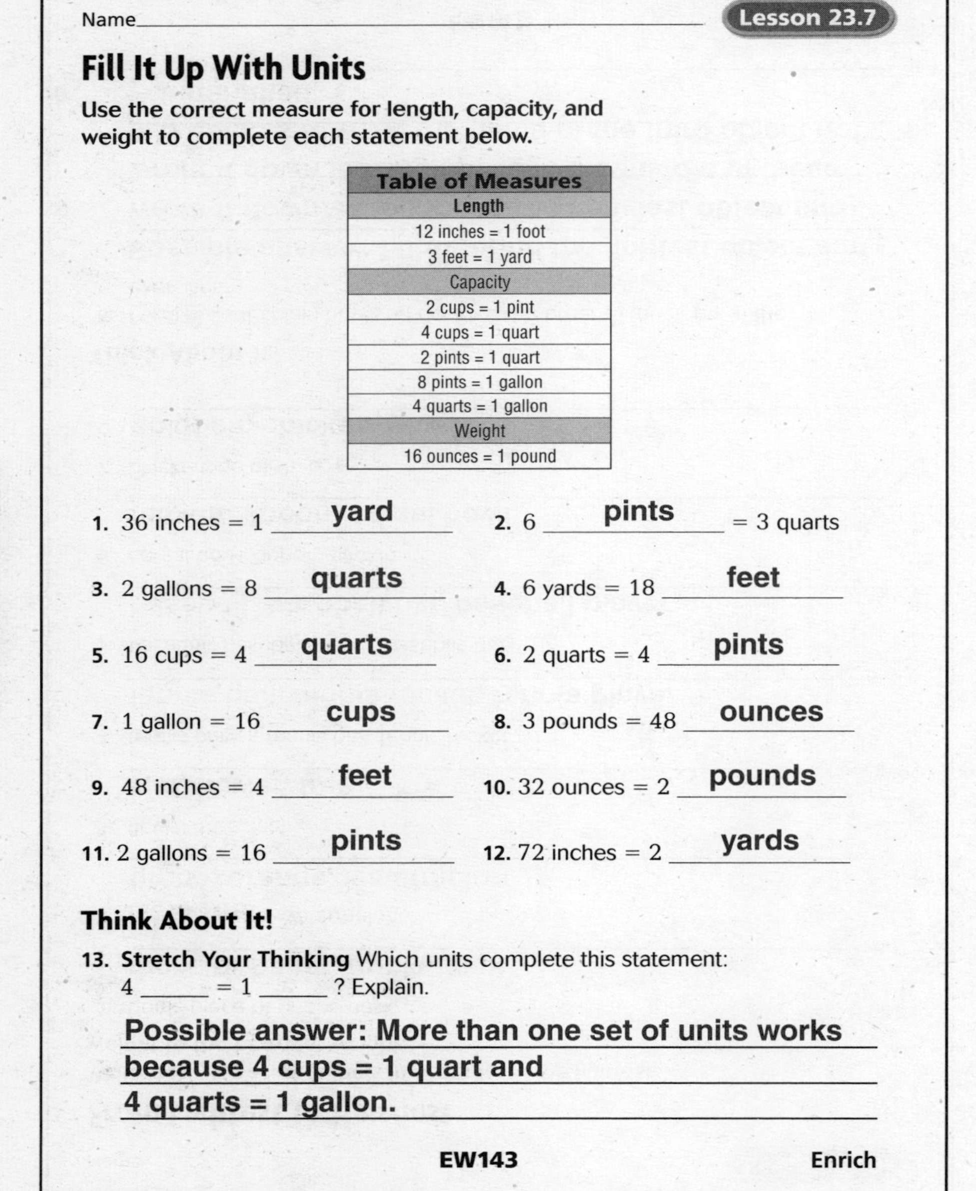

Name______________________ **Lesson 23.7**

Fill It Up With Units

Use the correct measure for length, capacity, and weight to complete each statement below.

Table of Measures
Length
12 inches = 1 foot
3 feet = 1 yard
Capacity
2 cups = 1 pint
4 cups = 1 quart
2 pints = 1 quart
8 pints = 1 gallon
4 quarts = 1 gallon
Weight
16 ounces = 1 pound

1. 36 inches = 1 **yard**

2. 6 **pints** = 3 quarts

3. 2 gallons = 8 **quarts**

4. 6 yards = 18 **feet**

5. 16 cups = 4 **quarts**

6. 2 quarts = 4 **pints**

7. 1 gallon = 16 **cups**

8. 3 pounds = 48 **ounces**

9. 48 inches = 4 **feet**

10. 32 ounces = 2 **pounds**

11. 2 gallons = 16 **pints**

12. 72 inches = 2 **yards**

Think About It!

13. Stretch Your Thinking Which units complete this statement:
4 ______ = 1 ______ ? Explain.

Possible answer: More than one set of units works because 4 cups = 1 quart and 4 quarts = 1 gallon.

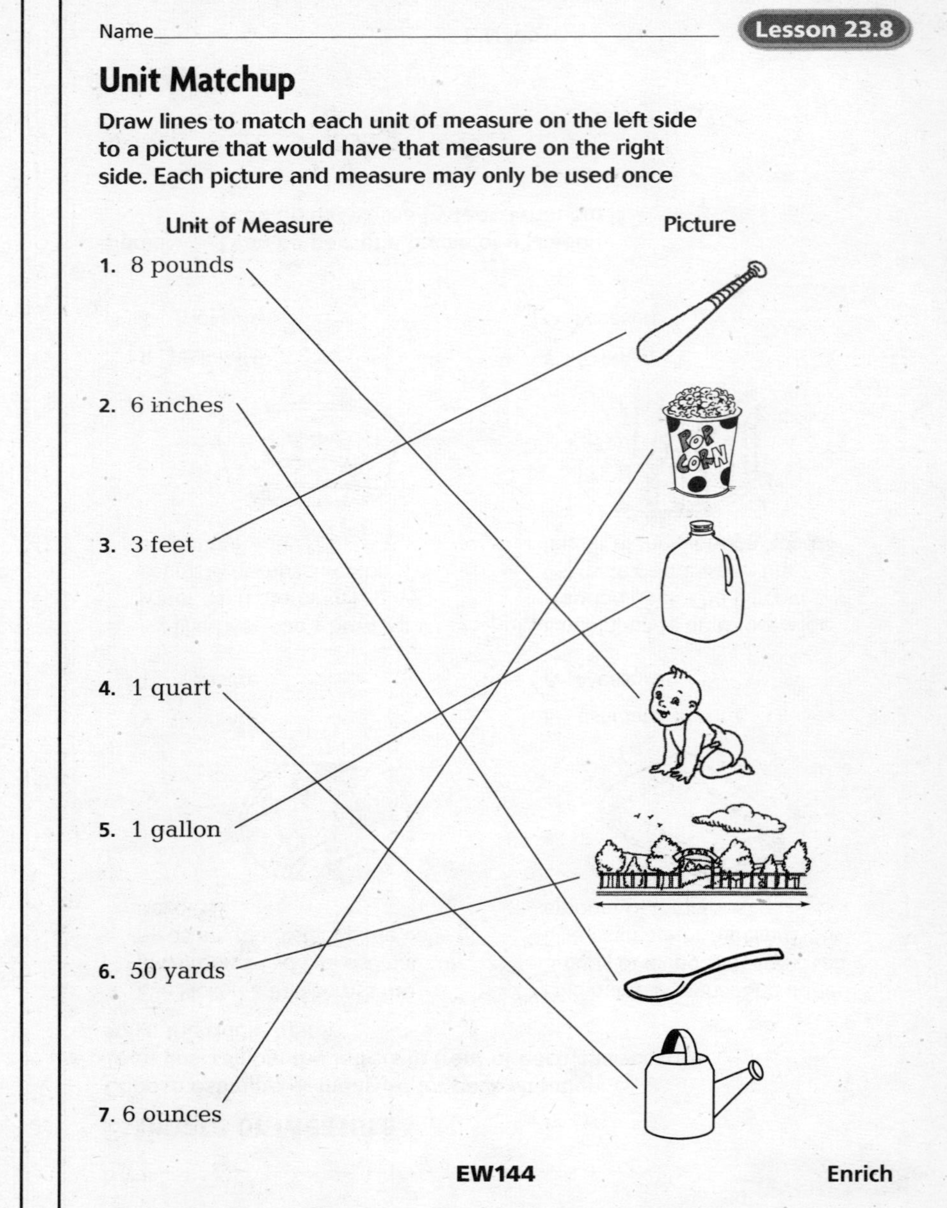

Name______________________ **Lesson 23.8**

Unit Matchup

Draw lines to match each unit of measure on the left side to a picture that would have that measure on the right side. Each picture and measure may only be used once

Unit of Measure **Picture**

1. 8 pounds

2. 6 inches

3. 3 feet

4. 1 quart

5. 1 gallon

6. 50 yards

7. 6 ounces

Name________________ Lesson 23.9

Fahrenheit Matches

Draw lines to match each thermometer with the correct temperature.

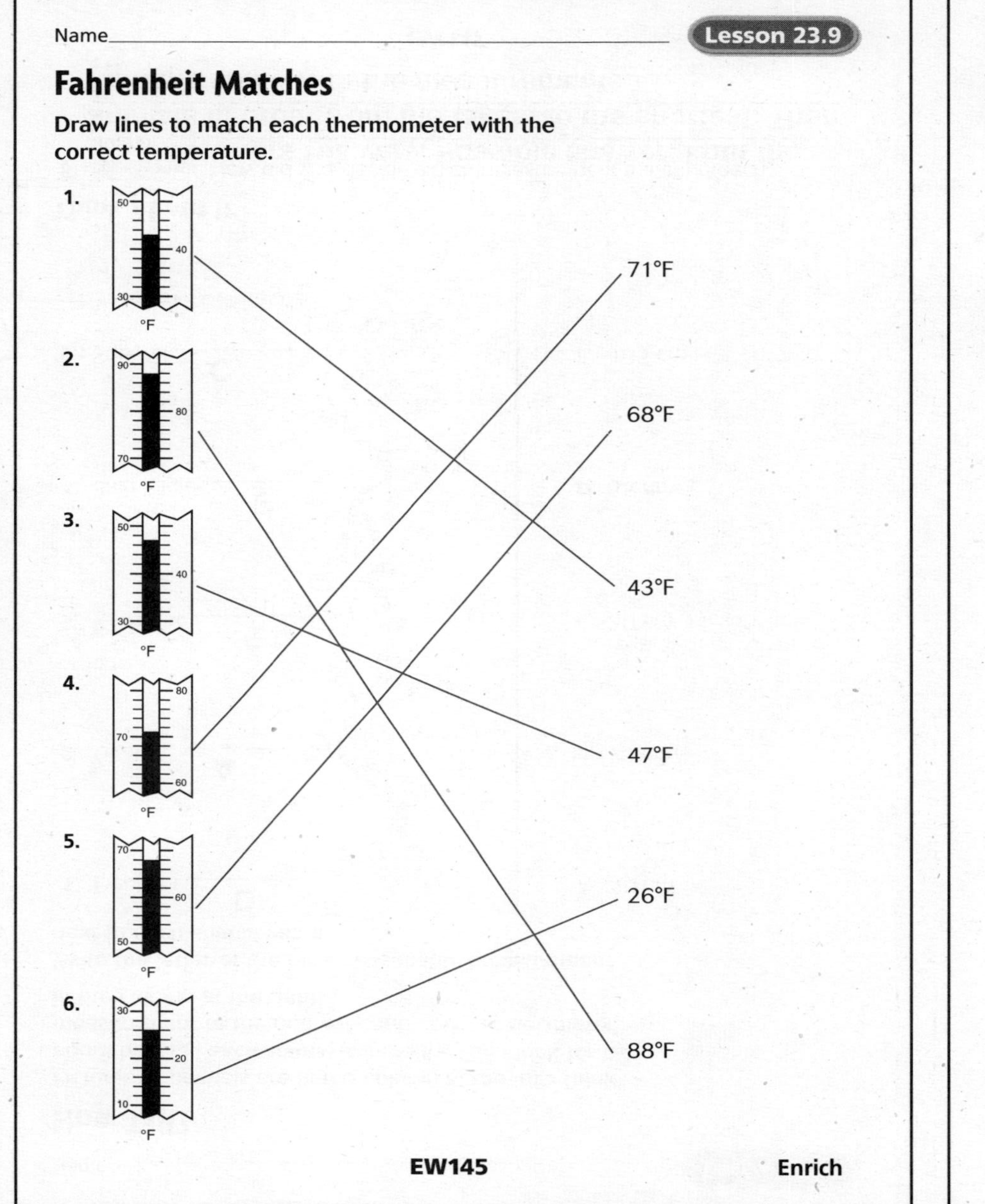

Name________________ Lesson 24.1

Old-Fashioned Units of Length

Here are some old-fashioned units of length.

Digit	about 1 centimeter
Span	about 1 decimeter
Ell	about 1 meter
League	about 2 kilometers

Read the story. Decide where each old-fashioned unit of length fits into the story. Write *digit, span, ell,* or *league* on each blank.

Eight-year-old Timothy awoke one rainy morning and put on his raincoat and boots. Each boot was 20 digits long. He walked through his front door, which was 9 spans wide. He remembered to take his 1- ell -long umbrella.

Timothy called his dog, "Buddy". He put Buddy into a red wagon that was 13 spans long. Then Timothy set off down the street, holding his umbrella and pulling Buddy along in the red wagon.

Timothy and Buddy met Mrs. Nicely, who was 18 spans tall. She gave Timothy a stick of gum that was 4 digits long. She gave Buddy a big dog biscuit that was 1 span long. Timothy said, "Thank you." Then Timothy and Buddy went on their way.

"Look at that big building," said Timothy to Buddy. "It must be 150 ells high. Did you know that there is a building just like it 3 leagues away in the next town?" Timothy and Buddy next went to the firehouse to look at the fire engines. Timothy's favorite fire engine was 20 ells long.

Timothy and Buddy strolled around for a while and then headed home. Timothy had to pull the red wagon with Buddy in it up a hill that was 60 ells long to get home. Back home, Buddy went into his dog house, which was 100 digits long. Timothy went right to sleep on his 3 ells long bed.

Name______________ Lesson 24.2

How Tall?

Pictures of animals are in the column at the left. Think about how tall each animal is inreality. Then look for its measurement to the nearest centimeter or decimeter in the column at the right.

Write the letter of the most reasonable measurement next to each animal name.

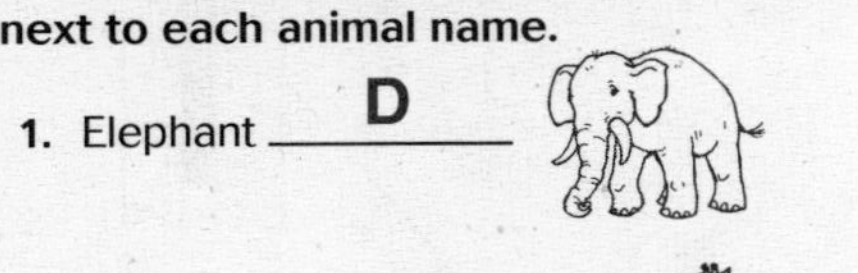

1. Elephant **D**
2. Giraffe **A**
3. Kangaroo **E**
4. Bald Eagle **B**
5. Squirrel **C**

A. 55 dm
B. 70 cm
C. 30 cm
D. 35 dm
E. 165 cm

Think About It

6. WRITE Math How did you decide which measurement matched each animal? **Answers will vary. Possible answer: I put the animals in order from the tallest to the shortest. Then I did the same with the measurements.**

Name______________ Lesson 24.3

How Far Did They Go?

Decide whether the units the students below are assigning to the distances they traveled are correct or incorrect. Write correct or incorrect. If the units are incorrect then write the correct units.

1. I walked to the store. It took 3 minutes to reach the store. I must have walked 300 kilometers. **incorrect; meters**
2. I drove for 2 hours to finally reach the concert late that evening. I must have driven for 120 kilometers. **correct**
3. I walked to the school. It took 20 minutes to reach the school. I must have walked 1,000 meters. **correct**
4. I rode the bus to a museum. It took an hour to reach the museum. The bus must have traveled 60 km. **correct; meters**
5. I ran to the mall from my house. It took 30 minutes to run to the mall. The mall must be about 2 km away. **correct**
6. I walked to the end of the block. It took 3 minutes. I must have walked many kilometers to reach the end of the block. **incorrect; meters**

Think About It

7. WRITE Math How did you find the answer for exercise 3? **Possible Answer: I thought about how long it would take to walk one hundred meters, then multiplied by 10.**
8. **Stretch Your Thinking** If question 3 had read, "I must have walked 100 centimeters," would the answer change? If so, how? **Yes; the answer would then read: incorrect; meters**

Who Has Which Container?

Andy, Bonnie, Charles, Doreen, and Frank have a lemonade stand. They each have a different size of container. The containers hold 250 mL, 500 mL, 750 mL, 1 L, and 2 L.

Andy does not have the lemonade container with either the greatest or least capacity.

Bonnie's lemonade container has a capacity of 1 liter.
Charles's lemonade container holds less than 1 liter.
Doreen's lemonade container holds 500 milliliters.

Use the clues from above to fill out the chart below. Write either *yes* or *no* in the correct box. Remember that when you write *yes* in a box, you should write *no* in all the other boxes in the same row and same column.

	250 mL	500 mL	750 mL	1 L	2 L
Andy	no	no	yes	no	no
Bonnie	no	no	no	yes	no
Charles	yes	no	no	no	no
Doreen	no	yes	no	no	no
Frank	no	no	no	no	yes

Use the filled-in chart to answer each question below.

1. Whose lemonade container has a capacity that is twice as great as Doreen's lemonade container?

Bonnie's lemonade container

2. Whose lemonade container holds 750 mL less than Bonnie's lemonade container?

Charles's lemonade container

3. Whose lemonade container has a capacity that is 1,250 mL less than Frank's lemonade container?

Andy's lemonade container

4. Whose lemonade container has a capacity that is half the capacity of Frank's lemonade container?

Bonnie's lemonade container

Come to Order

You can list objects in order from least to greatest mass or from greatest to least mass.

1. List the adult animals below in order from greatest to least mass.

Alligator Rabbit Sheep Rhinoceros

rhinoceros, alligator, sheep, rabbit

2. Name a different animal, with a mass that is less than that of the third animal in your list but greater than the mass of the fourth animal. **Possible answers: dog, raccoon**

3. List these adult animals in order from least to greatest mass.

Chimpanzee Giraffe Skunk Whale

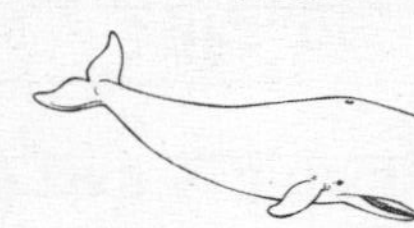

skunk, chimpanzee, giraffe, whale

4. Name a different animal, with a mass that is greater than that of the second animal in your list but less than the mass of the third animal. **Possible answers: cow, horse, zebra**

Think About It!

5. WRITE Math Suppose you have two closed boxes. One box is about 4 times as large as the other. Each box is filled with one or more objects. Just by looking, could you tell which box has the greater mass? Explain your answer and give an example.

No. Possible explanation: Sometimes smaller objects have a greater mass than larger objects. For example, a small box filled with coins would have a greater mass than a much larger box filled with feathers.

Name________________ Lesson 24.6

Capacity, Length, and Mass Analogies

An *analogy* is a group of related words. For each of the following exercises decide which object will complete the analogy. The first exercise is done for you.

Example

The length of a rake is to the length of a bar of soap as the length of a car is to the length of a/an ☐:

A bus (C skateboard)
B soccer field D city street

Explanation

Longer	Shorter
rake →	bar of soap
car →	skateboard

1. The capacity of a bathtub is to the capacity of a mug as the capacity of a liter is to the capacity of a **C**:

   A sink C milliliter
   B bathtub D pool

2. The length of a shoe is to the length of a penny as the length of a book is to the length of a/an **C**:

   A bed C eraser
   B bus D baseball bat

3. The mass of an apple is to the mass of an encyclopedia as the mass of an encyclopedia is to the mass of a **C**:

   A grain of sand C boulder
   B pebble D quarter

4. The mass of an elephant is to the mass of an ant as the mass of a car is to the mass of a/an **A**:

   A bowling ball C house
   B bus D jet airplane

Think About It

7. WRITE Math Explain how you found the answer to exercise 2.

   Possible Answer: I know a penny is shorter than a shoe so I found the answer that is shorter than a book.

6. **Stretch Your Thinking** If exercise 4 had read:

   The mass of an ant is to the mass of an elephant as the mass of a car is to the mass of a/an ☐:

   Which answer choice/s would be correct? **B, C, D**

Name________________ Lesson 24.7

Measurement on the Mythical Isle of Ik

The natives of the mythical Isle of Ik are known as Bliks. Bliks have developed their own system of measurement. This system is shown in the table of equivalent measures below.

Length	Capacity
5 biks = 1 tik	500 miks = 1 kik
50 biks = 1 jik	
10 tiks = 1 jik	**Mass**
500 jiks = 1 rik	500 ziks = 1 nik

Several Bliks made statements about their measurement system to tourists who came to the Isle of Ik. Use the table above as a reference, write correct or incorrect for each statement. If the statement is incorrect, rewrite it to make it correct.

1. Jolik said, "25 biks = 5 tiks." **Correct**
2. Sulik said, "500 ziks = 2 niks." **Incorrect. 1,000 ziks = 2 niks.**
3. Kalik said, "300 tiks = 3 jiks." **Incorrect. 30 tiks = 3 jiks, or 300 tiks = 30 jiks.**
4. Yorik said "3 kiks = 1,500 miks." **Correct**
5. Palik said, "8 jiks = 20 tiks." **Incorrect. 8 jiks = 80 tiks, or 2 jiks = 20 tiks.**
6. Golik said, "100 biks = 2 jiks." **Correct**

Think About It!

7. WRITE Math Would you rather use the Ik system or the metric system of measurement? Why? **Answers will vary. Possible answer: The metric system. Because the metric system is based on tens, it is easier to change between units.**